BUILDING

with

PAPERCRETE

and

PAPER ADOBE

A Revolutionary New Way to Build Your Own Home for Next to Nothing

Gordon Solberg

An Earth Quarterly Book

ISBN 1-928627-02-1

Published by
Remedial Planet Communications
Box 23
Radium Springs, NM 88054 USA
505-526-1853   earth@zianet.com   www.zianet.com/earth
Laura Solberg, publisher • Gordon Solberg, editor

Printed in the United States of America.
SECOND EDITION.

An Earth Quarterly Book

CONTENTS

Thanks

I want to thank my wife, Laura Solberg, for her unfailing love, support, hard work, enthusiasm, and positive energy. She was an integral part of the interview process for this book—she ran the tape recorder and asked questions, while I took the photographs and asked questions. She also spent many hours transcribing tapes.

I also want to thank Mike McCain, Eric Patterson, and Sean Sands for sharing so freely of their time and expertise. Without their innovative thinking and hard work, there would be nothing for me to write a book about.

Thanks also to all the **Earth Quarterly** readers for your letters of support. You continually inspire me to keep plugging away at all this.

Introduction

Papercrete is essentially a type of industrial strength paper maché made with paper and cardboard, sand, and Portland cement. The concept is quite simple—you build a mixer (essentially a huge kitchen blender), mix the dry ingredients with water to form a slurry, cast the slurry into blocks or panels, and let it dry. When it hardens up, papercrete is lightweight (it's 80% air), an excellent insulator (R 2.8 per inch), holds its shape even when wet, and is remarkably strong (compressive strength of 260 psi). And, since it contains paper fibers, it has considerable tensile strength as well as compressive strength. Papercrete is a remarkable building material, and is remarkably inexpensive, since all the ingredients (except for the cement) are free or nearly free.

This country wastes a criminal amount of paper and cardboard each year. Americans aren't even making a pretense of recycling most of it. Our landfills are clogged with trash. Millions of people have substandard housing. Papercrete offers a way to turn "trash" paper and cardboard into inexpensive houses that are strong, well insulated, and easily built. Papercrete can simultaneously reduce our overuse of landfills while providing affordable housing for millions of people. This is an elegant, win-win solution to these two problems.

Laura and I have known about papercrete since the mid 90s, but to us it was just another fringe building technique, and we didn't pay much attention to it until early 1998, when we started hearing about some people living at an intentional community called City of the Sun near Columbus, NM who were building houses out of recycled newspapers and magazines. This sounded like an intriguing idea, and we decided to do an article about it for *Dry Country News,* the magazine we were putting out at the time. Then a friend of ours visited the paper house builders, and returned all excited and enthusiastic about what they were doing. Our curiosity was now totally aroused, and we asked our friend if she would be willing to take us down there to meet the builders and see what they were up to. We went to City of the Sun, met the builders, and our lives haven't been the same since.

What we found, when we first visited City of the Sun in March of 1998, was a couple of experimental builders—Mike McCain and Sean Sands—who were more than happy to show us what they were doing. We were impressed. These guys weren't just talking theory, they were building real houses out of paper. Sean's little 300-square-foot guest cottage was almost complete, and Mike had completed the walls for the circular, 1000-square-foot house that he was building. When they told us how much the materials for the houses were costing them—less than $1.00 a square foot—we knew that they were doing important work that deserved to be broadcast at a national level. And so *Earth Quarterly* was born.

Papercrete was originally patented back in 1928, but it was too cheap and simple to be profitably marketed at that time, so it fell by the wayside until recently. It has been independently rediscovered by several experimenters, beginning in 1983. It's so new that people haven't even settled on a name for it yet. Mike McCain calls it **fibrous cement**. Eric Patterson, who independently discovered it in 1990, calls it **padobe**. Other people call it **papercrete**. This is the name I eventually settled on, since this is the most "user friendly" name to my ears.

Laura and I visited City of the Sun twice more during the spring of 1998, and I wrote a long article about papercrete which appeared in *Earth Quarterly* #1, our special "Paper House Issue." During the summer of 1998, Laura and I built our own papercrete mixer, and started work on *Earth Quarterly's* papercrete office. After mixing up dozens of mixerloads of slurry, we realized how ridiculously simple the process really is—it's very similar to working with concrete, except that papercrete is much less heavy, and is much easier to work with. During the summer we also visited Eric Patterson, the granddaddy of active papercrete pioneers, and learned a lot from him.

In the fall of 1998, we visited Crestone, CO, where Mike McCain had spent the summer building several papercrete houses, and developing some amazing production capabilities. When we saw what seemed like acres of papercrete blocks and slabs drying in the Colorado sun, we realized the enormous potential of papercrete when people are seriously motivated to crank out the tonnage. We were impressed.

In the spring of 1999, we visited Sean Sands again at City of the Sun, and were brought up-to-date on his latest project, **paper adobe**, a substance which has been pioneered by Bill Knauss of Tucson. Paper adobe is a mixture of dirt, paper and water, which hardens into a durable block that has a considerably higher insulating value than plain adobe. Being lighter in weight, it is easier to work with. And, since all the ingredients are free or almost free, Sean has reduced his materials cost down to a remarkable 16¢ a square foot. He has every expectation that he will be able to reduce his materials cost to zero. If that's not revolutionary, then I don't know what is.

This book contains of all the papercrete articles from the first four issues of **Earth Quarterly**. We are also including University of Arizona architecture professor Mary Hardin's article on paper bale construction, since it is another innovative way to utilize "waste" paper as a building material.

This book is not a connect-the-dots builder's guide. We do plan to work closely with both Eric Patterson and Mike McCain to produce a couple of builder's guides, and hope to publish at least one of these during the summer of 1999. We also plan to have a video out by May 1999. Please check our web site <www.zianet.com/earth> for the latest developments.

This book is intended to be a thorough presentation of the papercrete and paper adobe concept from as many different angles as possible. Using this book, a clever builder will have more than adequate information to build his/her own papercrete house.

We need to emphasize that **papercrete and paper adobe are experimental!** Mistakes have been made, and will continue to be made. Because they are so new, there is no proof that papercrete and paper adobe will stand up to the elements for the long term (20 years or more). However, it seems reasonable that if proper precautions are taken, that papercrete and paper adobe will last indefinitely.

Laura and I are excited to be associated with papercrete and paper adobe. There is probably enough paper and cardboard thrown away each day in this country to build a small town. Once papercrete catches on, it has the potential to revolutionize the building industry, an industry which desperately needs to make a quantum jump from the 19th to the 21st Century.

Intro to the Second Edition

It's been three years since I put out the first edition of this book. The original edition sold out over a year ago, and has been out of print until now. I have been selling an info packet that contains almost all the information in this book, but there has always been a demand for me to provide a "real" book. Now, thanks to the miracle of on-demand publishing, I am finally able to put out the second edition of this book.

The first edition contained all the papercrete information in **Earth Quarterly** 1-4, plus about half the information in EQ #5. This edition adds the rest of EQ #5, plus all of **Papercrete News # 1 and 2**—an additional 48 pages.

This book is a reprint of the original magazine layout. In some cases I had to remove ads which are no longer relevant. And occasionally the magazine pages contained parts of other articles which had to be removed. So this book contains some blank spots. Rest assured that these blanks are intentional, though it might not look that way!

This book also contains some new information that has never been printed before: the article about the innovative papercrete roof design; the "flooding experiment" article; and several smaller articles here and there.

—March 1, 2002

Build your own home for $1000 (or less) using **FIBROUS CEMENT**, a revolutionary new building material

SHELTER DREAMS

Shelter is the most compelling element of any lifestyle. The need for shelter is hard-wired into us, no doubt because our ancestors (or more accurately, non-ancestors) who didn't seek shelter at night tended to get eaten by the leopards and hyenas. Only the "shelter seekers" survived to produce offspring, and we are their descendants. So it's no surprise that we all have dreams about "the perfect home," along with our other dreams of perfect health, perfect happiness, perfect prosperity, and the perfect fulfillment of our souls.

Our shelter fantasies begin when we are very young. Put some young children into a room with a chair and a blanket and what will they do? They'll drape the blanket over the chair and create their own little shelter, along with a fantasy world to go with it.

After we become adults, our shelter fantasies become more substantial, and much more expensive. Most Americans seem to have bought into the myth that a "real house" must be very large and very expensive, requiring a multi-hundred-thousand-dollar mortgage and the better part of a lifetime to pay off.

A minority of Americans (who **Earth Quarterly** is designed for) have a more penetrating insight into the whole "shelter question," and we ask ourselves questions like, "Why should houses be so large? Why should they be so expensive? Why should they waste so many resources? Why should we have to enslave ourselves for the rest of our lives just to have a decent house? Why do contractors, bankers, realtors and escrow agents drive big fancy cars?" After we answer these questions to our satisfaction, we get to the biggest question of them all: "What can we do about all this?"

THE POWER OF BUILDING OUR OWN HOMES

There have always been people (such as the readers of **Earth Quarterly**) who have a "can do" attitude. We figure that we can do just about anything we set our minds to.

For example, we can even build our own homes! (What a revolutionary concept this is in modern America, where "consumers" (who are more helpless than they would like to admit) are unable to provide for their most basic needs, such as food and shelter.) When we build our own homes, we **empower ourselves** in a way that merely paying off a mortgage never can.

When we build our own homes, we reconnect with part of our own sacred birthright, and we discover that we were designed to be **at home** on this planet. We are **supposed to be here**, and **it comes naturally to us!** We are not just mere "consumers," or expendable cogs in some corporate machine—we are **part of Nature!** We possess, if we will but tap into it, the **inner wisdom** required to live on this planet in the way that Nature intended. We are **inherently competent** to build our our own homes, grow our own food, develop our own livelihoods, and live in genuine communities—and when we do this, we are then able to share the benefits of our existence with our friends, neighbors, and community-at-large. Rather than being just a bunch of alienated consumers, each jealously protecting our own narrow self-interest, we have the potential within us to create a genuine civilization that goes beyond the mere accumulation of monetary wealth and the distractions it provides.

I think our Founding Fathers were correct when they included "the pursuit of happiness" as one of our inalienable rights, but I think we need to emphasize, in today's "couch potato" era, that a vital component of true happiness is being **competent in the natural world**, and that this type of happiness isn't necessarily to be found in spending all day working at a meaningless or semi-meaningless, pre-programmed job and then going out to a movie at night "to unwind." Being competent to fill a narrow niche within the System is all well and good for people who are drawn in this direction, but not everyone is going to find fulfillment there.

I think millions of Americans are hungry to be doing something more real, more meaningful, more soul-fulfilling with their lives. Getting down to the physical nitty-gritty of actually building a home is an excellent place to start. It's not "the answer" in and of itself, but it is definitely a start.

PAPER HOUSES

There are many ways to build an inexpensive shelter, depending on where you live, and what kinds of materials you have available—the most common alternative building materials include some combination of rocks, dirt, concrete, logs, straw bales, old tires, and... paper.

Did I just hear somebody mention paper? This is preposterous! What could be more ridiculous than a paper house? Remember the story of the Three Little Pigs, and how the Big Bad Wolf huffed and puffed, I mean, seriously now, can you imagine what the Big Bad Wolf would have done to a **paper** house?

Well, let me explain. A paper house isn't made out of sheets of paper blowing in the wind. Instead, it's built with a type of industrial-strength paper maché called **fibrous cement**. Basically what you do is take a large mixing vat, soak old magazines and newspapers until they're soft, and then mix together a soup of 60% paper, 30% screened dirt or sand, and 10% cement. Then you take this glop and either (1) make it into blocks or slabs, (2) pour it into forms directly onto your wall, (3) plaster over existing walls, or (4) use it for mortar. (It's possible to use straw or even dried grass to supply the fiber if paper is unavailable. Cardboard can also be used—its only disadvantage is its bulk.)

When dry, fibrous cement is lightweight, an excellent insulator, holds its shape well, and is remarkably strong. It is resistant to being crushed (compressive strength) and to being pulled apart (tensile strength). (Regular concrete, on the other hand, has high compressive strength but no tensile strength to speak of, which is why it usually has to be reinforced with steel bars, called "rebar.")

Fibrous cement is highly fire-resistant. Since the individual paper fibers are saturated with cement, oxygen doesn't have a chance to penetrate, and combustion cannot be sustained. I tried an experiment, aiming a propane torch at a fibrous cement block to see what would happen. The block charred on the surface where the flame hit it, but it didn't burn after several minutes of direct flame. A piece of 1x2 lumber, by comparison, burst into flame within a few seconds of being torched.

Consider some figures: Fibrous cement has a compressive strength of 260 psi, without sand in the mix. Adding sand triples the compressive strength. An 8-foot-high, one-foot-thick wall of fibrous cement has a load bearing strength of 15 tons per running foot, yet weighs only 120 pounds per running foot! An elaborate foundation is not necessary, because the weight of a wall amounts to only one pound per square inch! The insulating value of fibrous cement is considerable—its "R" value is 2.8 per inch. This means that a 12" wall has an "R" value of 33.6, which is impressive by any standard.

In addition to increasing the compressive strength, there is another—astounding—advantage to adding sand to fibrous cement—you end up with a substance that has a high insulating value and a high thermal mass, all in one package. There is no other building material that can make this claim. How this works is: each individual grain of sand embedded in the "matrix" of fibrous cement is surrounded by insulating air pockets and paper fibers. Because of all that insulation, it takes a relatively long time for heat to flow from one sand grain to another. Since the sand is distributed evenly throughout the mix, you end up with "the ultimate thermal flywheel effect" which is amazingly efficient—a fibrous cement wall will take all day to warm up, and all night to cool down. Even if fibrous cement wasn't so cheap, it would be revolutionary for this reason alone.

Factoring in (1) low cost, (2) high tensile strength as well as high compressive strength, (3) high insulating value and (4) high thermal mass, we definitely have here a substance that has the potential to create a revolution in the construction industry. It's about time!

One advantage of working with fibrous cement is you don't have to worry too much about how much water to add to the mix. With regular concrete, if you add too much water, the final product will be weaker than it should be. With fibrous cement, the cement is absorbed by the paper fibers, insuring that it is evenly distributed throughout the mix, and any excess water simply evaporates or oozes into the ground.

When dry, fibrous cement can be sawed with a chain saw or a bow saw, so you can build your walls first and add windows and doorways later wherever you want. You can screw into it or sand it. The blocks can be keyed, and fitted together later. It's amazingly versatile stuff.

If fibrous cement is so great, then why didn't somebody invent it a long time ago? As a matter of fact, someone did—it was originally patented in 1928, but it was too cheap and simple to be profitably promoted, so it fell by the wayside until recently.

PAPER HOUSE VISIONARIES

In its most recent incarnation, fibrous cement was independently developed by Mike McCain in Alamosa Colorado, and Eric Patterson of Silver City, New Mexico. McCain, an irrepressibly enthusiastic inventor, built three fibrous cement houses in Colorado before meeting Patterson in New Mexico. The two exchanged ideas and creative ferment, and then McCain took his expanded vision to the City of the Sun, an intentional community in southern New Mexico, 4 miles from the Mexican border.

There he met Sean Sands, a retired MD who had just arrived from his summer home in British Columbia, and within hours they were starting work on two fibrous cement houses at City of the Sun—Mike wanted to build a house for his mother, and Sean wanted to build one for his son. So with a lot of focused enthusiasm, a minimum of money, and tons of old newspapers and magazines they obtained at the local landfill, they set to work, in November of 1997, to turn their dreams into reality.

Now it's time to look at some pictures:

Sean Sands' House

First, we'll look at Sean Sands' project. The key piece of equipment in his paper block "factory" is the mixer, which consists of 55-gallon drum with a lawnmower blade in the bottom, powered by an old pickup truck for which he paid $150. What he has created here is a huge version of the everyday kitchen blender, and it works on the same principle—the "glop" gets sucked down the center of the blender to the blades, then returns up the walls to the top, where it is pulled down to the blades again, over and over until the right consistency is obtained. In this photo, Sean adds wet newspapers to the mixer. The old truck which powers the mixer is on the right side of the picture, and on the bottom-left corner is one of two 55-gallon drums in which newspapers and magazines are soaked until they are soft. In the background is a wall of fibrous cement blocks drying in the sun.

Here's another view showing him adding a shovelful of cement to the mixer. Each batch requires 1 shovel of cement and 3 shovels of sifted sandy dirt to a drum of newspapers and magazines. "Glossy" magazines work fine—in fact, they are preferred, because the "slick" magazine paper contains clay, which is beneficial to the mix.

Another view showing, from left, (1) the two soaker drums filled with newspapers and magazines, (2) the mixer, and (3) the old truck that powers the whole contraption. One soaker drum of paper will make 20 blocks.

When the batch is ready, he unplugs the opening at the bottom of the mixer and lets the slurry ooze out. Wearing rubber gloves, he spreads the slurry evenly over the draining tray, which allows excess water to drain out. The draining tray consists of a sheet of corrugated steel curved into a U-shape. Over that is a layer of chickenwire, and a layer of plastic shade cloth. Each batch makes 5 or 6 blocks, which he calls "bunker blocks" because they are made with sandbags, and retain the sandbag shape when dry.

9

While the slurry drains, he readies two plastic sandbags. The sandbags are inserted into 2-foot lengths of 6" galvanized stovepipe, and each stovepipe rests in a 5-gallon plastic bucket.

Then, after inserting a funnel, he shovels slurry into the sandbags.

The sandbags are placed inside a wooden form.

Then he tamps them down with a hoe. This results in a denser, more evenly-filled block. The form can be removed immediately and then, after 12 hours of drying, the bag can be peeled away from the block. The sandbags are reused indefinitely. The blocks are then stacked to dry for several days, at which time they can be used for construction.

Standing in front of a wall of blocks drying in the sun. Sean holds a finished block with one hand to show how light it is. Each block weighs approximately 15 pounds, and contains 10¢ worth of cement. All other ingredients are free—talk about cheap! Sean views block making as a form of meditation. Many repetitive jobs can become deadly dull after awhile, but for him, making blocks is part of a highly goal-oriented process that engages his full energies (he is not just making blocks, he is building houses).

This house contains no wood, which helps to explain its low cost. The main arches were formed with wire "livestock panels" curved into position and covered with 1" chickenwire. Then the wire was covered with a slurry of well-drained fibrous cement. After curing, he then laid down a layer of "bunker blocks" and covered this with more slurry. The only reason for using wire at all is to hold up the fibrous cement as it hardens. Once the fibrous cement cures, it makes a very strong roof. Sean and Mike are experimenting with casting curved roof panels on the ground, then lifting them into position when they are dry. Such a method would require no wood or wire to build the roof of a house, and a roof would go up very quickly.

Sean plans to add a final, water-resistant coating to the outside of the house. Ordinarily, he adds 1 shovel of cement, and 3 shovels of sandy dirt to a batch of paper slurry. To make his surface coating, he plans to experiment with the following mixture: to a load of paper slurry, he will add 2 shovels of cement, 2 shovels of lime, 6 shovels of clean sand, and possibly salt as a hardening agent. This, he says, will give him a hard, water-resistant, surface-bonded, final coating.

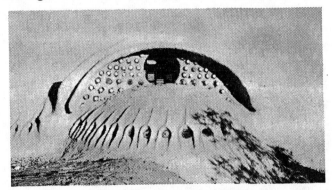

Here's another view of Sean's house. There is no foundation—the house is built directly on bare dirt. Much of this house is underground. Rather than digging the hole first and the building the house around the hole, he built a low wall with the roof over it first, and then went in and excavated the inside of the house. This, says Sean, has advantages:

"This allows you to get a structure up very quickly, and then go under, where you have a microclimate. It's sheltered from the sun, the rain, the freezing, and you can work all day inside without any discomfort. With conventional construction, if you're stuck with your building half up, it's deteriorating, you're spending money for commuting, paying rent for accommodations, you might lose heart because it takes too long. This way, our aim is to get up the structure as quickly as possible and as cheaply as possible, and then you've got a place you can stay, and you can work inside, night and day, in any sort of weather, and you're protected."

These colored glass blocks make a nice skylight at the top of the house. It's too bad this picture isn't in color, because the blocks are beautiful shades of red, blue and green.

Here's a view from inside the house, looking out the main entrance, showing some of the 150 bottles inserted into the walls for light. The interior of the house has a snug, cavelike feel. There are no right angles in this house—all surfaces are curved.

11

Mike McCain's House

The system that Mike McCain developed for his house has considerably more capacity than Sean's. The mixer consists of a stock tank, 7 feet in diameter and 2 feet high, with a lawnmower blade at the bottom. Since he was able to buy a used tank, the entire setup cost him only $65.

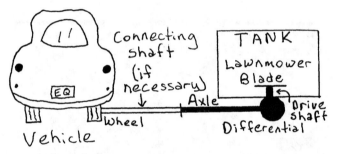

This diagram outlines the power train for the mixer. The same basic arrangement is also used for Sean's mixer. Any combination of junk car axles, driveshafts, and differentials will work just fine.

Here's a close-up showing how he connects the van's axle to the mixer. Any working vehicle can be used as a power source. There are many ways to hook up a vehicle to a mixer, Mike says. The important thing is to include a U-joint to compensate for any misalignment between the vehicle's axle and the mixer driveshaft.

While the tank fills with water, Mike adds old magazines and newspapers to the tank. Cardboard works as well—but it has the disadvantage of being bulky. He doesn't pre-soak the papers—they become soaked very quickly once they are in the tank.

This is the tank after he's put in the right amount of paper. The tank is still filling with water, and most of the paper is still floating on top of the water. It will sink once it becomes saturated.

After the mixing tank is full of water, he starts up the van, puts it in gear, and lets the mixer churn. This picture was taken immediately after he started mixing, and the sheets of paper are still pretty much intact. It takes a lot of torque to mix a batch this size, Mike says. This van has a 350 cubic inch engine, which Mike says is about right for turning a 22" lawnmower blade. When he powers the mixer with his Toyota van, which has a smaller engine, he uses a 16" blade.

While the mixer runs, he fills 8 or 9 5-gallon buckets 2/3 full of sandy dirt. Each bucket contains about 6 shovels of dirt. He strains out the larger rocks with 1" chickenwire. Bigger rocks, he says, tend to tear up the lawnmower blade. Here he adds a bucket of dirt to the slurry. Notice that the paper has already started to break down.

Then he adds a bag of cement to the mix. Ordinarily, he uses one 94-pound bag of cement per load. In this instance, he was going to make blocks to be used at the very top of his house, and he wanted extra strength, so he added two bags of cement to the mix.

After the slurry has mixed long enough, he unplugs the drainpipe sticking out of the bottom of the tank, and lets the mixture flow into a garden cart. This particular load took

about 1/2 an hour from the time he first started adding paper and water till the time he started emptying the slurry from the tank. The slurry can also be pumped into forms. Or, most efficiently of all, a paper block factory could be built on a hillside, where gravity would do most of the work.

Mike decided to make "brownie blocks" with this batch. Just like brownies, which are baked in a pan and then cut up afterwards, the fibrous cement slurry is dumped into a drag form, sets for about an hour, and is then cut into blocks. Here, Mike shows his drag form. It consists of 10-foot-long 2x6s spaced 3 feet apart. On the top of the form is a piece of plywood which smooths off the top of the slurry as the form is dragged along. The two little blocks of wood automatically score the slurry, so he later knows where to make his cuts.

Here he dumps a load of the slurry into the drag form. Notice that some of the slurry has slopped over the edge onto the ground. Mike is not concerned about this—unlike concrete, where any spillage quickly hardens into unusable rubble, spilled fibrous cement can simply be mixed into the next batch.

Now he's almost through with the batch. Using a tape measure, we found that one batch, when spread onto the ground like this, is 3 feet wide, 40 feet long, and about 6 inches deep. Mike isn't concerned about how thick the blocks are—if they're a little skinny, he simply uses a bit more mortar when laying them into place.

After the slurry has set up for about an hour, he uses a brush cutter and slices the mix lengthwise along the score lines.

Then he takes a square-ended shovel and slices through the mix perpendicular to his first cuts. Voila, the "brownie blocks" are done, and are ready to be put onto the wall after curing for 4 more hours. Mike estimates the outer wall of his house amounts to about 8 batches like this.

The house that Mike is building for his mother is 40 feet in diameter and 8 feet high. This picture was taken on March 3, 1998, when the walls were almost completed. The inner room, which will be the bathroom, is designed to support the roof timbers. The foundation is an 8-inch-deep trench filled with rocks. He will cut openings for the windows after the walls are completed. The walls of this house, by the way, required about 6 Toyota van loads of old newspapers and magazines.

Although the walls are strong and solid, they are actually 80% air! Mike looks at it this way: the slurry starts out as 80% water, so after the water evaporates, the hardened fibrous cement is 80% air by volume. Of the "solid" 20% of the volume (which is what we see in this picture), Mike estimates that it consists of 1/2 sand, 1/4 paper, and 1/4 cement by weight.

By March 21, he had the roof timbers in place. The roof design he favors would use no wood at all. Instead, it would be built like a suspension bridge—steel cables would radiate out from a central vertical pole to anchors in the ground (see diagram on next page). However, somebody gave him these used telephone poles, so he decided to use them instead.

This house has several exciting characteristics. First, consider the low cost—Mike estimates that the total cost of materials for this house (walls, roof and floor, but excluding windows and doors) is $600. for a house with over 1000 square feet of floor space! That's 60¢ a square foot! Thus, the 75¢ per square foot figure headlined on the front cover of this issue is actually quite conservative.

Additionally, a house like this can be built with amazing speed. Mike estimates that, using his large mixer and an efficient method of getting the slurry into the forms, 1 or 2 people could manufacture enough blocks in a day to build 4-5 houses. Then, after the blocks are manufactured, a crew of 4-6 people could build a complete house like this—walls, roof and floor—in just one day. It's amazing what can be done with a material that is lightweight, easy to work with, and structurally strong.

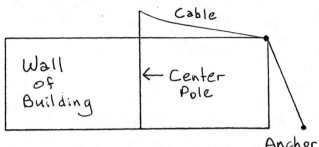

By April 11, Mike had most of the wire on the roof, ready to be covered with fibrous cement. First, he laid a spiral of steel cable on top of the roof timbers. Over that, he laid 6x6" reinforcing mesh (ordinarily used for reinforcing concrete floors), covered with 1" chickenwire.

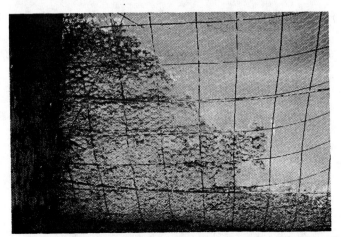

This closeup from the bottom shows all the elements of Mike's roof. On the left is a roof timber. Steel cables span the gaps between the timbers. Over the cables is 6x6"

reinforcing mesh, and over that is 1" chickenwire. Fibrous cement slurry is pumped directly onto the chickenwire. After that sets up, fibrous cement slabs will be laid on top of the slurry, and the slabs will be covered with yet more slurry. After the slurry is dry, he will cover the roof with $65 worth of hot tar, which will soak into the fibrous cement for a permanent bond. Ordinarily, hot tar just puddles on top of the roof rather than soaking into the roofing material, and is subject to eventual cracking.

This detail shows how the roof timbers are attached to the wall. Rebar is driven several feet into the wall, bent around the timbers, and then nailed down.

Converging roof timbers cast a vivid shadow pattern on the bathroom wall. When the roof is finished, there will be a skylight in the center. Photo by Sean Sands.

This is another innovation—a "jumbo block" that is 4 feet long, 2 feet high, and 1 foot thick. If you're going to use blocks, why make a bunch of little blocks when you can instead make a smaller number of big blocks? It takes these "jumbo blocks" several weeks to cure, but then they can be easily handled by two people, and a wall can go up very quickly. They are keyed at the ends so that mortar can be packed tightly in between adjacent blocks, making for a very strong joint. Or, 4x4 timbers can be inserted between the blocks if desired.

This is Mike's slip form. Slip forming is the quickest, easiest, and most elegant way to build a circular wall, because there is no need to manufacture blocks first. Talk about quick! To build a round house, all you need is a center pole, a length of rope, and a slip form. Attach the slip form to the center pole with the rope, and it is easy to build a perfectly round wall by keeping the rope tight.

This is ideal for a one-person "construction crew"—by the time you work all the way around the circumference of your house and are ready to start the next layer, the first layer will have dried sufficiently to support the weight of the second layer. Mike recommends adding 2 feet to the height of the wall on any given day (which he says will take only a couple of hours). Then, let it cure for a couple of days before adding the next couple of feet. Using this method, Mike estimates that one person could build a house like this with about a week's worth of labor, though it might take several weeks total when you factor in curing time and other delays.

This picture shows some of the interior plaster work. His favorite method for applying the plaster is to pat it on with his hands (notice the finger marks in the plaster at the bottom of the picture, next to his leg). Ordinary stucco offers hardness, but no strength to speak of, so it has to be applied over lath or chickenwire—otherwise it tends to eventually flake off the wall. Fibrous cement, because it has considerable tensile strength, actually makes the wall stronger after you apply it. Incidentally, fibrous cement can be used to repair eroded adobe buildings—not only does it fill the cracks, it makes the wall structurally stronger and insulates it as well.

Sean's Domes

Ian Sands with the dome form (bottom) and a row of dome blocks (top). The form is 9 feet long, and the 9 tapered blocks constitute one "section" of the dome. There are 16 sections in a dome. It takes 3 pours of his mixer to make one section. One $6 bag of cement will make 2 sections.

Sean stands in front of the partially-completed versions of his latest project—fibrous cement domes. In addition to being incredibly strong, the dome shape offers the maximum amount of inside volume and floor space per square foot of wall. These domes have an inside diameter of 14 feet, and a floor area of 154 square feet. Total purchased materials per dome (which includes bricks, mortar and plaster): 10 bags of cement x $6 per bag = $60 per dome. This works out to 39¢ per square foot!

Sean recommends building 3 domes at once to optimize your efforts. He estimates that it would take 4 days for one person to make the blocks for 3 domes, and about 5 more days to build the domes. On the first day of building, you can lay 3 courses of blocks for all 3 domes. On subsequent building days, you can lay a couple of courses of blocks per day.

The 3 domes can be connected together with passageways to make a 500-square-foot house. Total materials cost would be about $180. Sean estimates that if you include everything—materials; fuel to run the mixer; trips to the landfill to collect newspaper; the value of your labor; and the amortized cost of your mixer—the cost for a 3-dome house would be about $1500, which is still remarkably inexpensive by today's inflated standards.

The dome on the right was constructed with bunker blocks; the dome on the left used "dome blocks" which will be described in more detail below. To facilitate completion of his bunker block dome, Sean decided to pour a fibrous cement "cap," which is lying on the cinders on the left side of the picture. The hole in the center of the cap is for a skylight.

This photo shows how the dome form is curved. The angled ends cause the bricks to lock together when they are mortared into place.

Neil Solberg shows that even an 8-year-old can handle a fibrous cement dome block.

Once you get to the top courses, the dome blocks are hanging out there in midair, and need to be supported by tent poles for about half a day until the mortar sets up. After the dome is completed, Sean will dig out about 2 feet of dirt from inside the dome, creating more headroom, and lowering the living space to a more protected underground location. Sean points out that one advantage of dome construction is the speed with which a house can be constructed—2 weeks, in his estimation. Then you can move in and be protected from the elements while you do the finish work.

Clusters of these domes could become a remarkable human habitat, particularly on hillsides—you could have indoor and outdoor passageways, stairways, courtyards, hidden nooks, overarching trees, sprawling vines, pools of water—the creative possibilities are endless. Such an environment would be cool in summer, and very tranquil.

This concludes our photo-essay. We will now return to the print portion of our presentation:

BUILDING CODES

Building codes started out with an idealistic purpose—to prevent contractors from foisting off sleazy buildings onto unsuspecting buyers—but have served, in the past 30 years, to inhibit innovative and low-cost homebuilding. I remember back in the late 60s reading about California hippies having problems with the building inspectors, who didn't like their domes and treehouses. And just last year I heard about a community in Oregon that was forced by the codes department to tear down their alternatively-constructed buildings. What a tragedy this must have been to the builders.

There are many rural areas where building codes aren't enforced, and you can basically get away with whatever you want. But there are many other areas with "activist" codes departments, where you can't get away with much of anything. With this in mind, I asked Mike about building codes, and this is what he had to say about his experiences:

The first time I talked to the building department [in Alamosa, CO], I went in there with a fibrous cement block I had made, and tried to describe all the advantages of my adobe-style block, and they were as courteous as they could be without telling me they didn't want to hear about it.

So I went home and thought about it. I researched what the official definition of adobe is, which is: "fiber and clay." There's no such thing as "adobe clay." It's the way clay is used that makes it be called "adobe." Now, the official definition of a "stabilized adobe structure" is "fiber, clay, and cement." Now the clever way we get clay associated with fibrous cement is, at the factory, when they make paper, they mix clay in with the paper to give you the slick paper for magazines and newspaper inserts.

The code doesn't specify a quantity of clay. Just "fiber, clay, and cement." What it does specify is a compression strength test that must be done. So I had one of my blocks tested. Then I took my compression strength test result, which cost $35, into the building department, along with the formula for my block, and the man just grinned from ear to ear, and took the photocopy of my test result, and said, "Yep, that's adobe; go get a permit!"

The idea is, bureaucracy doesn't want to make a decision. Now I went in there with an attitude. It was a bad attitude. I went in there to challenge them. I said, "This is the official definition of adobe, and this is my test result," and he just grinned from ear to ear. Now had he not grinned from ear to ear and told me to go get my permit, I was going to tell him, "If you stop me from doing this, I'm going to sue you, because you're obstructing my right to build out of a proven material." So I had an attitude.

The truth is, they love the idea of fibrous cement. They're just in a double bind. If they tell you, "Yeah, you should build out of fibrous cement," then they're recommending something that they become responsible for. If you go in there and take the decision out of their hands, they're happy to see you. They're not bad people. They just don't want to be in trouble. So it's a matter of attitude.

There's a downside to the code. Because you have to go by adobe standards, you're going to have to put in a lot heavier footer than you ever possibly needed for this material. They haven't realized that this material, because of its light weight, there's less than a pound per square inch weight on this wall touching the ground. They cause you to over-construct. That's just the way it is.

SOME THOUGHTS ON STRAW BALE CONSTRUCTION

While we were talking, Mike offered some of his observations on straw bale construction, and how it compares with fibrous cement:

I've done straw bale too, and I love the concept of straw bale, but the only advantage of straw bale, really, is insulation value. And it costs you too much. Because the super-wide footer you have to put down really eats you alive. And then you have to go post-and-beam, and that isn't cheap. And then after you get your walls up, then it's really hard to do the plumbing and wiring. Because you're talking about something that isn't structural to begin with, and so you have to be careful not to cut into the strings of your bales, and things like that. A straw bale house is really hard to plumb and wire.

Now in stick frame building, you just drill holes through the studs and put in the wires. How do you do straw bale? It really gets awkward to do the plumbing and the wiring in straw bale, because you're basically talking about a solid wall. And then you have to tie chickenwire mesh onto the bale, which means you have to poke stringers through there and tie them. It's very time-consuming and quite awkward, and very expensive. Chickenwire mesh isn't really cheap.

And there's the labor intensity of it. By the time you get done with the labor in a straw bale house, by the time you've paid the extra for the footer and the extra involvement, there's no advantage left to the straw bale. You've had to use a conventional floor and a conventional roof, and so all you've really saved is insulation in the wall. And you've made such a big, heavy, thick wall, you have a lot more mass than you actually need. It just doesn't pay. And with all the difficulties of construction, it's marginal.

Now the idea's good. And the walls go up real fast, but the finish work is so time consuming. Now with fibrous cement, I find you have all the advantages of straw bale: you have the lightweight, gigantic building blocks, but you also have structural integrity. You don't need post-and-beam. You have load-bearing capacity.

With straw bale, if you come to a window or door and the bale doesn't fit, you have to clip the bale, then tie it back, and go through a lot of hassle. If a fibrous cement block doesn't fit, you just take a saw and cut it in half. Or cut in the window after you get the wall up.

There's structural integrity to fibrous cement construction. There are no weak joints. With straw bale, you can't tie the bales together—there are joints. With fibrous cement, you're mortaring everything together, so it just makes one solid mass. You have the great insulation value with fibrous cement like you do with straw bale, but you can do it in one foot instead of 18". You can do interior walls out of fibrous cement a lot narrower than that. You still have soundproofing, insulation, and structural strength. You can do stuff with fibrous cement that you can't do with straw bale.

To do wiring, I just take a saw or a router and cut a groove where I want my wire, put my wire in it, and patch it with fibrous cement, and I'm done. And plumbing is the same way, and it's fully insulated. Even in the floor, when I make a slab of fibrous cement, you can just cut out a groove in the floor, lay your pipes in and patch it with fibrous cement.

Fibrous cement makes the most wonderful floor. Now you can pour a 4" slab of fibrous cement and 2" of concrete on top of it, and when you walk it, it doesn't feel like a concrete slab. It's still rigid, but the fibrous cement absorbs the impact. Now, because it holds a screw beautifully, and you can glue to it, you can just glue-and-screw a subfloor right on top of fibrous cement. You don't have any joists or anything to squeak. And you can just have a nice, traditionally-finished floor if you want. Or you can lay tile on it, whatever you want. What you have is a warm, comfortable floor, because fibrous cement is such a good insulator.

TERMITES

What about termites? Mike told of an individual who performed a little experiment:

A person buried a board and a piece of fibrous cement side-by-side in a known termite area, and the termites just absolutely devoured the board, and they didn't touch the fibrous cement at all. And it's logical, because there's no food value left in the paper pulp. Everything of any value has been leached out in the paper-making process. There's no oils, no solvents, nothing with any food value. And so it isn't attractive to termites. And then you surround the paper fibers in cement, and you're talking about something that's downright untasty to a termite.

WET CLIMATES AND ROT

I asked Mike about the possibility of fibrous cement rotting in wet climates. He told me about one of his fibrous cement buildings in Alamosa, CO, which is used for raising snails commercially. The inside of the building must be kept at 85°, and a humidity of 90%. To keep the humidity high, the owner soaks the fibrous cement floor with a hose—he soaks the front half of the floor for six months at a time, then switches to the back half. "After 2½ years," Mike said, "there isn't a bit of mold anywhere on the walls of that building, and the soaking has had no effect on the floor."

WATERPROOFING

Fibrous cement absorbs water, so precautions must be taken to prevent this, especially in wet climates.

First of all, it's common sense, in wet climates, to always build on a "high and dry" foundation. Keep the fibrous cement off the ground, so that it doesn't "wick up" unwanted moisture.

There are several ways to waterproof the outer surface from rain. Sean's low-cost formula for his final finish coat is printed on page 6 of this issue. As mentioned on page 10, Mike likes hot tar for the roof, since it penetrates into the fibrous cement and doesn't crack.

Mike also recommends Elastomeric plastic coating, and "Homestar" silicone-based sealer. I think that ordinary latex paint would work very well for the walls. However, the first coat or two would probably soak into the fibrous cement, and it might take several coats before the paint job looked decent.

CONCLUSION

After going to the City of the Sun three times for this article, and watching Sean and Mike's projects evolve, Laura and I have become fibrous cement believers. We are already building our own mixer, are accumulating vanloads of newspapers which our local daily paper is happy to get rid of, and plan to build a fibrous cement building or two this summer.

To us, it will be a special thrill to turn our junk mail into building blocks. Junk mail is such an in-your-face reminder that in this culture, we don't even have to <u>do</u> anything to accumulate trash—we merely have to <u>exist</u>, and trash comes to us automatically. It will be a new, and gratifying, experience for us to say, "Oh, goody! Another building block!" whenever a bundle of junk mail appears in our mailbox.

For our next issue, we plan to print a complete, piece-by-piece description of our 55-gallon electric mixer. We will also print full construction details of our new buildings. We hope to build a barrel-vault roof in segments on the ground, and will lift the segments into place and plaster over them for extra strength and insulation value. There will be virtually no metal in these buildings, and the only wood will be for the door and window frames. We are really looking forward to our summer construction projects, and we hope that future articles in **Earth Quarterly** will answer any questions you might have about this marvelous new building technique. Till then—happy building!

FOR MORE INFORMATION

Mike McCain has written a book about fibrous cement (reviewed in this issue). A video will be out shortly.

A Third World Portable Mixer

rear end does," Mike says, "so there are plenty of rear ends to be found in Mexico."

Personally, I think that this design is just too cool. The driveshaft of a car makes the wheels turn, but it also works the other way—if you turn the wheels, the driveshaft turns. This mixer is designed to be towed behind just about anything—car, truck, horse, burro—and towing it causes the lawnmower blade to spin.

Mike has already made two major design improvements—(1) He will offset the PVC outlet about 45°, so that it is no longer at the very back of the mixer. This will facilitate dumping, since the drum can be tilted closer to the horizontal, and will also allow people to fill forms as the mixer is towed along, straddling the forms. (2) He will also add a hitching mechanism so that mixers can be coupled together, and a whole string of them can be towed at once. Towing a train of mixers through a small village would definitely be a community event!

Mike McCain has invented a Third World, portable mixer, consisting of (1) an oil drum, (2) a lawnmower blade, (3) a short length of PVC pipe, and (4) the rear end of an old car. This particular mixer is specifically designed to be used in Mexico. "The rest of the car usually wears out before the

Mike and Sean plan to start giving workshops in the fall of 1998.

For information on the book, video, or workshops, write: New Vision Building Unltd., Box 1331-EQ, Alamosa, CO 81101 or Box 695-EQ, Columbus,. NM 88029.

To reach Mike McCain by phone, call 505-531-2542 and leave a message.

To reach Sean Sands by phone (Nov-Apr) call 505-531-2579.

To contact Sean Sands during the summer (May-Oct) write him at Box 4-EQ, Grand Forks, BC, V0H 1H0, Canada.

AND SO IT CONTINUES

There is never any "ending" to an article like this. You just reach a point where it's time for this issue to go to press, so you just temporarily shut off the flow of information till next issue.

I thought I'd sneak in once last picture here, showing Sean Sands' latest domes, built since I was there last on April 11. The two domes on page 12 are on the extreme right-hand edge of this pictures. The two partially-completed domes in the center of the picture represent one day's work by Sean, with a little help from his son, Ian. The amount of productivity one person is capable of, given the right expertise and the right materials to work with, is just incredible. Notice the tent poles holding up the inward-leaning walls until the mortar dries. We will definitely be printing a lot more about fibrous cement domes in future issues.

MORE THOUGHTS ON STRAW BALE CONSTRUCTION AND "WASTE"

Mike McCain's comments about straw bale construction on page 19 created some controversy after they appeared in **Earth Quarterly**. We received several comments from professional straw bale builders, including one point-by-point refutation of almost everything Mike

said about straw bale construction.

We feel that Mike is entitled to his opinions, which is why we printed them. We printed his words in italics to make absolutely clear that these were his words, and not ours. (We use a tape recorder, and make transcripts of the tapes, to ensure that what we print is accurate.) I think it is redundant to urge people to take everything with the proverbial grain of salt, because I think people already do that. It is also unnecessary to urge people to read widely and draw their own conclusions, because they already do.

I regret if anybody thinks that I am anti straw bale, or that **Earth Quarterly** is anti straw bale, because this is not the case. Papercrete and straw bale construction are not in competition with each other. Each have their place in the greater scheme of things.

While we're on the subject of straw bale construction, I need to point out an important issue that straw bale proponents tend to ignore. Straw is often promoted as an "agricultural waste product." Yes, this is true to the extent that farmers follow poor agricultural practices.

However, ideally straw would be plowed back into the soil, not turned into houses. This would improve the health of the soil—tilth, fertility, micro-organism content—all are enhanced when you add organic matter to the soil.

Too few modern farmers, and particularly grain farmers, follow this philosophy of returning the vital organic matter to the soil. Instead they rob the soil of organic matter. They either burn the stubble, or bale it and sell it to people who want to build houses with it. But this is a short-sighted attitude. As John Jeavons pointed out in EQ #3, "By not taking care of our soil and land first, we are not taking our own needs seriously. We look at short-term solutions, but we forget about the very basis upon which our life depends: our soil."

If we are to develop a truly sustainable society, we need to get away from the concept of "waste." We delude ourselves into thinking that it is possible to "throw something away," when there is no "away" to throw anything. We all share the same planet. Your pollution soon becomes my pollution. The waste that you "throw away" might end up in my backyard, and vice versa.

Ideally, there would be no "waste" paper to make papercrete out of. Ideally, all paper and cardboard would be recycled to make yet more paper and cardboard. That way, fewer trees would be cut down, and our planet would be able to breathe more easily. (I mean this literally—trees are the "lungs" of our planet.)

However, as long as our culture remains at its present primitive, waste-producing level, we might as well use our "waste" in a constructive fashion. If it comes down to a choice between burning stubble or baling it and building houses with it, then let's build houses. If it comes down to burying paper in a landfill or building houses with it, then let's build houses. But let's never forget our ultimate goal—to do away with "waste" entirely."

A Visit with Eric Patterson, Paper House Pioneer

Papercrete is not new—it was first patented in 1928—but it's so cheap and simple that there was no money to be made from promoting it. So the concept languished for many years. Eric Patterson, of Silver City, NM, rediscovered the process in 1990, and is the originator of the present paper house movement. On July 5, Laura and I spent 3 hours visiting with Eric, as he showed us his various papercrete projects.

Eric Patterson is a printer by trade. He owns and operates Unicorn Press in Silver City, NM. Print shops create a lot of paper waste, and this has always bothered him. It was Earth Day, 1990, that inspired him to do something more creative with his waste paper.

"Print shops throw out tremendous amounts of paper. It's mind boggling. Just cut scraps, mistakes, and everything else. Paper was always my concern, because I was dumping tons of it. We had an Earth Day celebration in the park, and it really got me to thinking. When I came home, I took all the paper out of the trash, separated it all, and then I decided to grind it up in a blender. So I did that, and then I was trying to figure out what I could do with it from there. Then I got the idea of mixing cement with it, thinking that you could make some kind of block. I took the blended paper and drained off the excess water, and then I mixed cement with the paper, thinking I was going to create this block. It didn't create a block. A week later, it was still squishy, so I thought it was a failure. I abandoned the project and forgot all about it. It dried in the sun and cured. I came back later and found it, and was amazed at what had happened to it. It was hard, and when I rapped on it, it had a high-pitched sound like I was knocking on a block of wood. I learned that paper blocks don't cure quickly like cement—they have to dry like adobe blocks before they become hard. It takes a long period of time to get the final product."

After much trial and error he developed an electric mixer, and started experimenting with different ratios of cement and paper. He started producing paper blocks in quantity, and went on to build a paper dome, a paper bedroom for his adobe house, and a paper privacy fence around his backyard. Word got out. Magazines wrote articles about him. He appeared in a documentary on PBS. At times his phone rang so frequently that he couldn't get his printing work done. He estimates that 1000 people have come to see him over the years. *"People always wind up coming to see me. The serious ones will always come here."*

Eric stands next to a pile of paper blocks made from print shop waste. His blocks contain only paper and cement. Each block contains about 1/4 shovelful of cement. He says it's important to add enough cement—without enough cement, the paper begins to break down when the block gets wet, and when it dries, you can pick it apart with your fingers. No matter what color paper his blocks are made from, they bleach out to a nice white color in the sun. *"My blocks are made with every kind of scrap paper that can possibly be used—pizza boxes, phone books, you name it."*

The form for these blocks is a .30 caliber ammunition can. He fills the can with slurry, and then dumps the block out to dry. There are holes drilled in the can so that the block can slide out. Without holes, a vacuum is formed, and the block will not slide out. The edges of each block are naturally beveled, which makes them perfect dome blocks. If you lay these blocks end-to-end, they will make an 18-foot circle. Eric is originally from Alaska, and used to build igloos out of snow, so the dome concept comes naturally to him.

This is his mixer, which is made from a plastic barrel. A 5-horsepower electric motor mounted vertically on the side of the barrel powers the twin s-blades he designed himself. There is a 2" pulley on the motor, and a 5" pulley on the blade shaft, connected by a v-belt. The rectangular steel box at the top of the mixer covers the pulleys and belt. That ragged black shape at the top of the mixer is a piece of black plastic for covering the motor. The slurry drains onto 1/8" hardware cloth suspended over corrugated steel sheets, visible at the bottom of the picture.

This mixer will make 4 blocks at a time. He can mix a batch in 4 minutes. The entire process—adding the water, paper and cement to the tank; mixing; and emptying out the tank—takes about twice that. *"If I really hustle, I can make probably 8 loads an hour. Which is not good enough for any kind of production work, but it's great for a little home operation. With my little system here, if I worked an 8-hour shift, I could turn out probably 100-150 blocks a day. Which would be enough to make money on, if you could sell them for a buck each. That's a little business. You could make $100 a day, but you'd know you worked. There's easier ways to make 100 bucks than that. But still, it's a business."*

He pre-soaks his paper to soften it. Some of the paper he uses is very tough. It's possible to mix slurry without soaking the paper first, but it's a lot more work for the mixer, and there will be little pieces of paper in the final product.

Here's a view showing the 20-foot-long draining tray, which empties into a stock tank. The slurry water which drains into the tank is pumped back up to the mixer, where it is reused. With this system, he recycles 80% of his water. He estimates that each block requires 10 gallons of water to make, so he recycles 8 gallons of that.

He recommends that blocks not be allowed to drain into the ground. *"The water that drains from the slurry has a lot of chemicals from the paper, and you will put contamination into the ground. I don't think it's really nasty stuff, but it would be better if you didn't do that. It's something we looked into with the environmental people way back, and there's some heavy metals that come out of the inks. Ideally you would have some kind of containment system so that any excess water will go back into a tank."*

His draining tray will hold a lot of slurry. He makes 4-5 mixer loads at lunch, lets it drain all afternoon, then forms it into blocks after work in the evening. The slurry can even drain overnight if the weather isn't too hot. If the slurry overdries, however, the cement sets up and the blocks tend to crumble after they have dried.

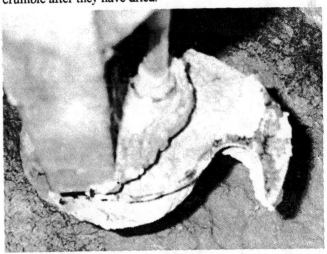

Eric has tried many types of blades over the years. He originally started with a boat propeller. But propellers are designed to move water, not for cutting. He learned that he was using up all his horsepower moving water around, with very little cutting action. The blades need to be slightly tilted, in order to create the proper vortex, but propeller blades are tilted way too much.

So the blades need a slight tilt to them—a flat blade just spins around without creating a vortex. What about the shape of the blade? The problem with ordinary blades with straight edges, he has found, is that paper tends to collect on the front surface of the blade, reducing cutting efficiency. He finally developed an s-shaped blade like the kind found in food processors. He is very happy with this design. The blades cut very efficiently, and are self-cleaning.

This is a lousy photo, because the automatic focus on my camera focused on the bottom of the tank rather than the blades. Nevertheless, some basic details are visible here. He has twin blades, 10" in diameter, spaced about 3" apart. His blades rotate counterclockwise—the point is the trailing end. The lower blade is covered with slurry, and barely shows in this photo.

23

Eric started by tracing the outline of a food processor blade onto a piece of paper. Then he enlarged the tracing with a Xerox machine so that it would fit a 10" circular saw blade. He traced the "s" outline onto the blade, and then took it to a welder, who cut the blade with a special cutting torch (saw blades are made with extra-strong steel, and are hard to cut).

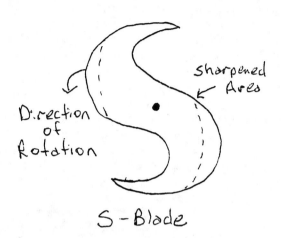

S-Blade

This diagram shows the basic shape of the blade. He heated the blade with a torch and put a slight twist to it, like a propeller, so that it would create a vortex. He also recommends bending one tip down and the other tip up, to increase the width of the cutting swath. Ideally, I would prefer to photograph one of these blades from several different angles so that the different bends would be more obvious. Hopefully I will be able to do this in a future issue.

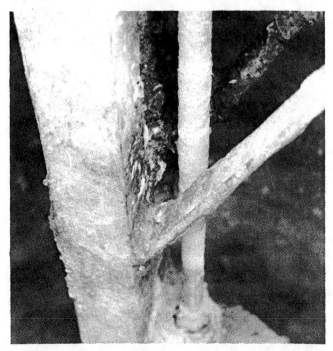

The blade shaft doesn't go all the way to the bottom of the tank. Instead, welded steel supports hang from the top of the tank. The blade shaft fits into a pillow block bearing attached to the bottom of the support assembly.

After the slurry has thoroughly drained, he carries it by hand to this steel mold that a welder made for him for $30. The dimensions are 12x16", and 4" thick. He has a wooden spacer in there because at the present time he is making 10" rather than 12" blocks.

The drained slurry he uses is very thick, so he can remove the mold as soon as the slurry has been packed into it. He pulls out the pin, and the mold is spread apart and lifted off the block.

A lot more people would build with paper if they didn't have to construct their own mixers first. Sometimes people ask Eric why he doesn't go into business building mixers for people. *"You can't 'just build equipment' in this country. You have to have it UL tested, and that's expensive— $25,000 to get something run through laboratories. Unless you've got a big company to hide behind, plus have the money to do the research, it's virtually impossible. If you just build equipment and put it out there, you open yourself up for tremendous trouble. If a blade came off, if anything went wrong, if somebody lost a hand, they're going to sue you."*

24

In the background is the 14-foot paper dome he built in the summer of 1991. The walls are 7" thick. In the foreground is print shop waste waiting to be turned into blocks. Each of these garbage bags full of paper will make 12 blocks. He's not making blocks fast enough to keep up with the accumulation of waste paper, so he plans to eventually build a 250-gallon mixer.

Eric has encountered moisture problems with his dome, because papercrete does not adhere to concrete. No matter what kind of caulking he tries, water gets into this crack between the dome and the concrete foundation and wicks up into the wall of the dome. It's a worst-case moisture scenario—water gets in very easily, but takes a long time to dry out. Water will not ruin the papercrete right away, but over a period of years will eat away and eventually ruin the bottom block.

This is what he is now trying. Galvanized roof edge is inserted into the crack, and Elastomeric coating is then painted over it.

When he built the dome in the summer of 1991, he covered the blocks with a papercrete plaster containing extra cement to make it harder. Originally, the dome had no coating over the plaster. Papercrete absorbs water literally like a sponge—throw a glass of water at a paper wall, and the water will be instantly absorbed. His uncoated dome became totally soaked after heavy rains. It got so saturated that he could press the papercrete with his finger at the bottom of the dome, and water would ooze out. The dome went through repeated saturation/drying cycles. But this caused no structural problems that he could see.

He has experimented with many different coatings over the years. This is what he now recommends (this information is worth a multi-year subscription to **Earth Quarterly**):

After the paper plaster dries, he paints on a coat of Homestar waterproofing sealer, which is silicone-based. *"It's the best thing I've ever found."* Thompson's doesn't work, because it is petroleum-based. Homestar sealer looks like water. He lets it cure for a couple of days after he paints it on. After it dries, you can spray it with water, and the water beads up and runs off it like it would off a highly-waxed car. After the sealer has dried, he paints the outside of the dome with Elastomeric coating, which he likes because its acrylic formulation gives it more stretchability than latex. But moisture will get through Elastomeric; hence the importance of using the silicone sealer under it.

It is possible to make your own silicone sealer, Eric says. To make it, you squirt two full squeezes of 100% silicone caulk from a caulking gun into a gallon of paint thinner, and stir it until it dissolves. This compound discolors in the sun and is not quite as good, but is a lot cheaper than the Homestar sealer.

Eric holds a patent on papercrete. We asked him about that. *"I have a patent, but I'm disgusted with the government. It's just terrible what they do to people. We spent $8000 getting this patent. We finally got it through, and we thought that, 'Hey, it's our patent!' and then guess what? Every couple of years they make you pay installments* *to keep it in force. Our first installment was over $600. And you just keep paying. You never own that thing. You're just renting it. It's just horrible. All it is, is another tax to screw you over. And nobody knows that. They never tell you that, anywhere. The patent people don't tell you that. Then all of a sudden out of the blue, it's 'you owe us more money.' So I told them, 'No I don't; you can have it.'"*

He talked about the Wright Brothers. First they invented the airplane, than they got a patent on it. Orville spent the next five years of his life going to court case after court case, trying to defend his patent. *"It wore him down to such an extent, that he died. They couldn't keep it under wraps. Imagine that, trying to keep the airplane under wraps! You can't do it. Anybody who saw it that had a little mechanical ability went 'Aha! I can do that!' It's the same way with paper blocks. I don't want to spend any time going to court cases. That's nuts, you know."* Eric has decided not to enforce his patent.

This counter inside his dome is made with papercrete. For a final coat, he recommends adding Elmer's-type glue to the slurry. When it dries, it can be sanded to a smooth finish.

This is the privacy fence he has built around his back yard, an attractive oasis of fruit trees, grapevines, and a small

garden. To keep this lightweight fence from blowing over in a high wind, he first drove steel posts into the ground every few feet. Whenever a block needed to be laid over a steel post, he cut a hole in the block with a reciprocating saw, slid it over the post, and mortared it into place. This created problems. Notice the vertical crack to the right of the wheelbarrow. Without the steel posts, the wall would have a chance to shrink and settle uniformly. But wherever there is a steel post, the papercrete that is touching the post is not allowed to settle along with the rest of the wall, and a crack forms. In the future, he will cut larger holes in the bricks so that they don't touch the posts, and this should eliminate the problem.

One advantage of a paper wall, Eric says, is that it doesn't soak up heat during the day, making for a much cooler yard in the evening hours.

Eric stands next to the 600-square-foot papercrete bedroom/living room he added on to his adobe home. He started work on it in 1992, and finished it in 1995. The walls are 12" thick, and he estimates that they have an insulating value of r 36. He has never done an official r-value test, but he did have some comparison tests done at New Mexico State University. In these tests, the papercrete had approximately the same r value as fiberglass insulation.

Paper houses are lightweight and flexible, so they would be ideal in earthquake-prone areas.

Eric says that this room can be easily heated with one little electric heater. It takes ten times as much energy to heat and cool the adobe part of his house as the paper part. The paper part of his house is so well insulated, that you can "heat it with a candle, cool it with an ice cube."

When adobe works best, Eric says, is when you have hot days and cool nights. *"During the dead of summer, when the nights are warm, adobe's the worst thing you can live in, because it soaks up tremendous heat during the day and cooks you all night."*

How about a paper dog house?

He built a picture frame around part of the original wall, to show what the house is made of. *"Otherwise, nobody would believe me."* To wire the interior, he cut a groove with a circular saw, inserted the wire, and plastered over it. For the electrical outlets, he traced around each outlet box, cut along the outline with a saber saw, then took a screwdriver and popped out the papercrete, leaving a perfect outlet-sized hole. He added sand to his mix for the stucco, so that it could be troweled. Straight papercrete without the sand tends to resist troweling. There was no need for chickenwire—paper plaster sticks very well to paper bricks.

If you didn't already know, you would never guess that this room is made of paper. Since papercrete absorbs outside noises as well as sounds coming from inside the room, it creates a wonderfully quiet ambiance.

Eric feels that inventors in this country are being stifled. There are too many inflexible rules and regulations. *"The whole system is bass-ackwards. Rather than being supportive, it constantly puts obstacles in your way."* The powers-that-be are desperately holding onto control and greed is automatically built into the system.

The trend of the future might very well be factories that produce paper blocks by the thousands. Eric talked about some Mennonite friends of his, who have a 250-gallon mixer, and plan to power it with the power take-off (PTO) from a tractor. Their whole goal is to make paper blocks for sale to the public. Eric has advised them to consider milling the blocks—make oversized blocks, and then cut them to the exact size you want. If all the blocks are exactly the same size, you can glue them together, and there would be no need for a mixer to make mortar. Imagine: building with paper without the need for equipment! This is an astounding prospect—you could order a truckload of blocks from your neighborhood paper block factory, buy a bucket of Elmer's-type glue and some paintbrushes, invite your friends over for a glue fest, and in a couple of hours you could glue together the walls of an entire house.

There's still lots to learn about papercrete, Eric says. People are inevitably going to screw up as they experiment with it. To the extent that papercrete aficionados communicate with each other and swap ideas, the learning curve will be enhanced for everybody, and mistakes can be avoided. There might very well be a Paper House Conference in the works. If this ever comes to pass, watch these pages for details.

You can reach Eric Patterson at 2115 Memory Lane, Silver City, NM 88061; 505-538-3625.

A Prototype Paper Block Factory

When Eric Patterson told us about his "Mennonite friends who are building a paper block factory," Laura and I knew that we would be doing an article about them for this issue. Here it is:

Travis Coffey lives with his wife, Amy, and their four children near the little town of Mimbres, New Mexico, which isn't really a town, but more of a collection of houses strung up and down the highway along the Mimbres River between the Black Range and the Gila Wilderness in the southwestern part of the state.

Travis supports his family by baking organic, whole-grain bread. He needed to have bread labels printed, so he went to the nearest town of any size, Silver City, and met Eric Patterson of Unicorn Press. The conversation eventually turned—as it often does with Eric—to paper blocks, and Travis immediately caught the papercrete vision. Being a baker who turns out thousands of loaves of bread every month, it just naturally occurred to him that maybe he could produce paper blocks by the thousands, as well.

Travis isn't really a Mennonite—people just need a label to pin on him, and "Mennonite" seems to fit. He and his family are associated with six other families in a church that has no name (because it needs no name) that meets in the homes of various members. The church members, who moved to Mimbres separately during the past few years, come from various backgrounds—Baptist, Church of Christ, Mennonite, Old Order Amish. *"The one thing that binds us together is our love for Jesus,"* Travis says. *"That, and what we think Jesus wants us to do—our values, our family goals."* It was to another member of this church community, Ira Beiler, that Travis turned for assistance in constructing the block-making machinery.

After months of experimenting and dealing with the finer points of Murphy's Law, they had finally managed to get their equipment working properly when Laura and I visited Mimbres on August 29. Here are some pictures that tell the rest of the story:

Travis stands next to his block-making equipment. The mixer consists of a 300-gallon tank with a blade in the bottom, powered by the power take-off from a tractor. When the slurry has mixed sufficiently to be made into blocks, it is released down the wooden trough into the "squish box." Excess water is squeezed out of the slurry by the hydraulic cylinder on the left. They have invested $1000 in the mixing unit, and $2000 in the hydraulic unit. Before all the bugs are ironed out and they have a fully functioning system, they expect to have $10,000 invested.

The tractor PTO is attached here.

The power from the tractor PTO makes a right-angle bend to the cutting blade via this gear box from a brush hog.

A stainless steel guillotine-type valve releases the slurry into the squish box. Notice the holes through which the excess water is expelled. Travis spent 4 weeks drilling over 8000 holes with a hand drill in his spare time.

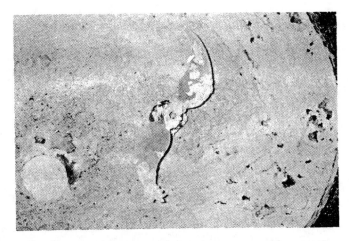

This is a fan blade, designed for blowing air, which he obtained from the "assets recovery" ("surplus sales") unit of a local copper mine. The blade, made of extra-tough alloy, is ideal for mixing slurry. It spins at 750 rpm. When the tank is filled to the top with water, the blade creates a vortex so strong that air is sucked all the way down to the blade. To make slurry, they add dry paper and cardboard boxes to the water, and the blade barely slows down at all. This mixer requires a lot of water to keep the vortex going, which results in slurry that is thinner than they would prefer. He wants to redesign the mixer so that it will make a thicker slurry. There is an advantage to this—the thicker the slurry, the less water that will have to be expelled by the hydraulic unit.

Here's another view of the squish box from above, showing the slurry entry port and many of the 8000 drainage holes. Travis says, "If for some reason we can't make paper blocks, we can sure make apple juice."

29

This close-up through the open door shows the steel piston that slides along the square pieces of steel, compressing the slurry into a block. The block, as you might expect, has two square holes in the center of it.

Here's a close-up of the 5"-diameter hydraulic cylinder, with an 8-foot stroke. It develops 60,000 pounds of pressure. They blew the frame apart several times before they welded on enough reinforcing gussets to withstand that much pressure. This unit compresses 9 feet of slurry into a one foot block. It blows geysers 30-40 feet into the air. (I will return some day when they are making blocks and take some pictures of this.)

The squish box has a hinged door, made of 1/2" steel, and held in place by two 5/8" steel rods. The finished block is removed through this door.

Travis shows two of his blocks drying in a nearby greenhouse. The dimensions of the blocks are 12x12x24 inches. He estimates that the blocks will have an insulating value of between R40 and R50. The blocks will weigh about 40-45 pounds when dry. These blocks are three weeks old, and still contain considerable moisture. He plans to construct a solar drying oven, 200-300 feet long, with black gravel on the bottom, some exhaust fans, and perhaps a condenser to retrieve the evaporated water so it can be reused. This solar dryer should reduce the drying time from 4 weeks down to one week. His goal is to produce 300 blocks a day (though 50 a day would be enough for now), so it's important to reduce the drying time—otherwise, he will have acres of slowly-drying blocks.

After the blocks are dry, they will be run through a gang saw—3 pairs of circular saw blades set 12", 12", and 24" apart—so that all six sides of each block will be sawed perfectly flat, and to exactly the right dimensions. This way, the blocks will all be exactly the same size, making it possible to quickly glue them together—preliminary tests indicate that the glue joint is stronger than the block itself. Travis estimates that a person working alone could glue together the walls of a house in 2-3 days. He says that these blocks offer some thermal mass and a lot of insulation—the best of both worlds.

His experiments show that the lower the cement content, the faster these blocks will smolder. The higher the cement content, the more fire retardant they are. Cement also makes the blocks unattractive to termites and other bugs. He plans to experiment with other binders—for example, he wants to develop a block that is 100% waterproof. He will develop a standardized formula when he gets into production.

There are two 5" holes in each block. He plans to design a hollow "bond beam block" for use at the top of a wall. This block will also have a pair of 5" holes. When the wall is completed, a concrete truck would come in, and would fill the bond beam blocks and all the other blocks with a single monolithic pour of concrete. *"You'd have a home that passes every code, because you're not asking the cellulose fiber to support the load. You're asking the concrete to do that—and they already have specs on concrete. That's nothing new. The engineers have had specs on concrete for years. We should be able to get these blocks to pass code without any difficulty at all. At least, that's what we're hoping. Of course, to begin with you still would have to go through the experimental building permit process which would require an engineered blueprint. Once we have enough empirical evidence, I think we can get these blocks to pass the Uniform Building Code, and once they pass that, any contractor can build with them."*

At the present time, Travis estimates that he will be selling his blocks for $7.50 each. The actual cost will depend on the productivity of his factory, and the cost of raw materials—newsprint in his area currently sells for $40 a ton. A 2000 square foot house will require 800 blocks costing $6000, but Travis points out that the blocks are a complete package—there's no need for framing, siding, or additional insulation, and it would be easy to cut grooves for wiring, which could be stuccoed over.

What does he call this stuff, anyway? In talking to Sean Sands, Mike McCain, and Eric Patterson, we noticed that they never actually called it "fibrous cement" or "papercrete" or whatever. They would point to it and say, "this material." So we asked Travis point blank: "What do you call this material?" And he answered, semi-tongue-in-cheek: *"How about 'Stabilized Cellulose Building Components'?"*

Travis feels that there is much more to his paper block factory than just the physical process of making blocks: *"If you find a need and you fulfill it, you'll have a market. That's what we have here. I think that our paper block company will grow out of love. Not only love for one another, but love for the planet, and love for our fellow man. All of that flows together to create something that's far more than a paper block. I don't like to get radical and overly spiritual, but I really believe that there's something real about products that are created under Heaven, under an open Heaven, whereas products that are created for greed, by greed, I think that those carry with them somewhat of a spirit that's not healthy."*

What does the future hold for the Mimbres Paper Block Factory? Travis is philosophical about this: *"Even if it's not in our future, paper block factories still will happen. I have no doubt about that. And I hope that it's in our future. I hope it's what we can do. If we don't, that's fine—there's still bread to make. And people still need to eat good bread."*

For more information about his paper block factory or his bread, you can write him at HC 68 Box 3031, Mimbres, NM 88049, or call him at 505-536-3263. I asked him what he would do if he got bread orders from all around the country, and he said that he would figure out a way to ship them. For blocks, be prepared to wait in line—he figures he's got two houses' worth sold already.

How to Build a Papercrete Mixer

WHY BUILD A PAPERCRETE MIXER?

Before a person decides to build a papercrete mixer, there are three factors that should be considered:

1. A mixer of my design, using new components, will cost about $350. You could buy a lot of straw bales for this much money. Maybe you would rather build with bales instead? It's possible to scrounge around for used tanks, electric motors, etc. and substantially reduce your cost. Or you could use a junk car axle and build a mixer for even less. Will you be building a large house, or several different structures? The more you plan to use your mixer, the lower the amortized mixer cost per structure will be.

Mixing up slurry and pouring it into molds to make paper blocks is the equivalent of mixing up concrete and pouring it into molds to make concrete blocks. Most people would much rather go down to the lumber yard and buy concrete blocks rather than make them themselves. Unfortunately, it is not yet possible to buy ready-made paper blocks. But when that day comes, we will look back to the present era and realize what a rough-and-ready, pioneer time it was, when people went to the trouble to build their own mixers and make their own paper blocks.

2. A papercrete mixer needs to be a rugged piece of equipment. Most people would never dream of building their own lawnmower or rototiller or compost shredder. There would be a lot more interest in papercrete if people could purchase a well designed, ready-to-use mixer. As one EQ reader pointed out, a lot more people can build houses than can build machines. But as Eric Patterson points out in this issue, there are severe liability risks for anybody who sells anything as potentially dangerous as a papercrete mixer.

3. Building a house with papercrete requires spending many, many hours having a very close relationship with your mixer. Many people who are drawn to a natural lifestyle would prefer for their relationships with machines to be more low-key. Low-key a mixer ain't.

With these thoughts in mind, we can now tune in to the experiences of our intrepid "inventor in spite of himself," the originator and chief victim of Remedial Planet Research and Development Laboratories:

A NO-BRAINER?

"This should be pretty much of a no-brainer," I confidently thought to myself as I prepared to build my mixer. After all, I had the electric mixer diagram from Mike McCain's *Fibrous Cement* book. All I had to do was buy all the parts, attach them together, and bingo!—I would be mixing slurry within hours! Or so I thought.

A BRIEF DIGRESSION

Before I get into the construction details, let's talk a bit about mixer options. I think that Mike McCain has absolutely the right idea—make a large mixer using a stock tank and a car rear axle that you can pick up for free or next to nothing, and power it with a vehicle. That way, you've got a rugged machine with a large capacity so you can do some serious mixing, you've got plenty of reserve power so your mixer can handle anything you throw into it, and you don't have to pay for a separate power source (which is the most expensive component of a mixer).

HOWEVER (and this is a big however), most people I've talked to simply don't want to mess with a large, vehicle-powered mixer, no matter how efficient and inexpensive it might be. Such a mixer is too big, heavy, and cumbersome to be moved easily. It's intimidating. And you get to breathe exhaust fumes while you mix slurry.

Most of the people I have spoken to would prefer a small, portable (or semi-portable), quiet, electric-powered mixer. You've got to mix a lot more loads of slurry to equal the output of a large mixer, but that's a tradeoff most people are prepared to live with.

A FRUSTRATING ORDEAL

My first mixer consisted of a 55-gallon plastic barrel, a couple of lawn edger blades on a steel shaft, and a 1-horsepower electric motor. A $30 coupler (a high price for such a small component, I thought) connected the motor with the blade shaft. The basic problem with this design is that there was so much vibration that the coupler always vibrated loose. I spent several days on this project, and many 35-mile round-trips into town, time and miles I really couldn't afford to spend. I became frustrated and hard to live with. Laura suggested that I throw the mixer into the river so that we could return to a more mellow way of life.

Finally I called Mike McCain at his fibrous cement hotline, 1-505-531-2201. He was very sympathetic and helpful. He told me that the design I was using wouldn't work. He suggested using pulleys instead.

DIGRESSION #2

Mike told me that a mixer is a deceptively simple piece of equipment. It's just an oversized kitchen blender, after all—what could be complicated about that? Motor, blade, and a vat to hold the slurry in—what's the big deal?

He told me that it was sheer luck that his first mixer worked at all. His next three mixers didn't work, and he found himself constantly returning to his original design. "If my first mixer hadn't worked," he said, "I would have given up and said that it couldn't be done."

Basically, every component in a mixer is interrelated. If you change one element, you change the entire equation. Various elements of a mixer would include the diameter of the tank, height/diameter ratio of the tank, diameter of the blade relative to the diameter of the tank, speed of the blade, and shape of the blade.

At the present time, mixer design is more of an art than a science. You have the option of throwing something together and fiddling with it until it works (or not), or you can copy a proven design. Mike gave me some good ideas that I utilized in designing my own mixer. This design can be improved upon, but hey—it works, and after all I went through with my first mixer, that's good enough for me.

LET'S HEAR IT FOR PULLEYS!

Until I built this mixer, I had always taken pulleys (and their connecting v-belts) for granted. Sure, I've changed numerous automotive fan belts in my day, and several pieces of my beekeeping equipment use pulleys, but frankly, I had never given pulleys much thought until it was my turn to actually design a machine with them. Pulleys, I learned, have several swell features: they allow you to quickly change the gear ratio of your machine; plus, the v-belt absorbs excess vibration and can compensate for a certain amount of misalignment between the pulleys. After my frustrating experience with the direct-drive coupler, I knew that I was going to be in pulley heaven.

I FIND A STOCK TANK

After I scrapped my original mixer, it was literally back to the drawing board, except for the 1-hp electric motor that I had already purchased. I did like the convenience of a 110 volt motor that I could plug into an ordinary socket. However, I recommend using a 2-hp, 220v motor which gives you twice the power for the same amount of current.

I liked the sturdy, corrosion-proof plastic barrel of my original mixer and its relatively low cost ($20). However, I didn't like the small capacity, and the curved bottom, which made it difficult for me to accurately align the bottom support flange (which will be explained later).

At a local feed store I found a cute little stock tank, 42" in diameter, and 24" high. Made of galvanized steel, it holds 135 gallons. It was nominally a 3-foot tank, but the feed store guy said that stock tanks are made in different sizes so that they can nest inside of each other for shipping. So I got a 42" tank for a 36" price. Such a deal. Including tax, the tank cost me a little under $90. Doubtless, a used stock tank could be purchased for much less, if you can find one.

ELECTRIC MOTORS

The type of motor to use is technically known as a totally enclosed, fan-cooled, reversible motor, 1750 rpm give or take. Like I said, I recommend using a 2-hp motor for this mixer design—you get double the power for the same amount of current, and a 2-hp motor doesn't cost all that much more than a 1-hp motor. It is a valuable piece of information to know that a 1-hp motor will work. It's not what I recommend, but it's what I use successfully every day.

An inexpensive source for a 2-hp motor is Northern, 1-800-533-5545. Once you are on their mailing list you will receive lots of junk mail from them—which can be used to make paper blocks. The motor to use is Item # 16178-C129. It costs $169.99 + shipping.

PUTTING IT TOGETHER

My goal was to use 100% off-the-shelf components if possible. (Eric Patterson's s-blade—described elsewhere in this issue—is an excellent idea, but very few people will be using blades of this design until somebody starts manufacturing them.) I decided to use a lawnmower blade as my cutting mechanism. An 18" blade was the smallest I could find in my local mega-building supply store, so I went with that. Since lawnmower blades have a 1" hole, I decided to use a 1" shaft, in this case a 16 gauge steel tube (not plumbing pipe). The shaft sits inside a 1" galvanized pipe flange mounted on the bottom of the tank to provide a stable base for the bottom of the shaft. This is Mike's design. It works fine, but a sealed bearing would be better. What happens with this design is, sand gets into the flange, increasing friction and reducing efficiency, which is especially noticeable in an underpowered mixer such as mine.

I had the local welder weld the pipe flange (with a 4" nipple attached) to the bottom of the tank. I also had him weld a 2" galvanized threaded coupling at the bottom edge of the tank, in case I ever decided to pump the slurry out. The total job cost me $20. The welder did an OK job, but he eyeballed it and the flange isn't perfectly aligned. Better, I think, would be to drill bolt holes through the bottom of the tank, and use a couple of rubber sheets (available at the hardware store) between the flange and the tank as a gasket to prevent leaking. Then, shims could be inserted where needed, to insure that the flange is perfectly vertical.

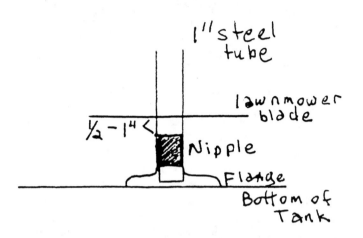

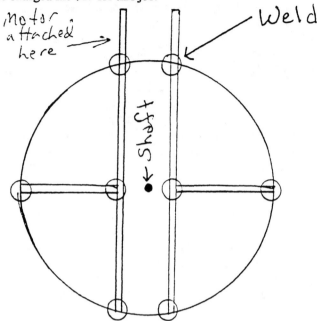

Weld angle iron to top of tank

angle iron with a hacksaw, marked the position of the angle iron with a magic marker, and took the tank back to the welder to have him weld the angle iron to the top of the tank. He charged me $15 for this job.

I learned, from my 55-gallon barrel experience, to align the shaft from the bottom up, not from the top down. I inserted the 1" shaft, with lawnmower blade welded to it, into the pipe nipple.

About the lawnmower blade: behind the sharpened leading edge, the blade is slightly curved. When welding the blade to the shaft, make sure this curve is <u>down</u>. This will force the slurry downward rather than up into your face. The local welder welded the blade to the shaft for $5.

Then I laid two pieces of angle iron (actually slotted steel), with the motor already bolted to it, across the top of the tank and spaced them equally on each side of the shaft. In the photo, notice the heavy piece of wood I used to counterbalance the electric motor. I sawed off the excess

Now it's starting to look like a mixer. I had an adjustable pulley on the motor when this picture was taken, which I decided not to use. I found that the cheapest way to wire the motor was to buy a 12-gauge, 25-foot extension cord on sale, cut off the female end, and attach it to the motor.

Now we're looking at some key details in the center of the mixer. It's necessary, when using pulleys, to have a bearing to hold the shaft in the right position. I used a 1" evaporative cooler "pillow block" bearing. To attach the bearing to the mixer frame, I first cut two pieces of flat steel and bolted them to the angle iron. Then I took two corner braces, bolted one side of the braces to the bearing's

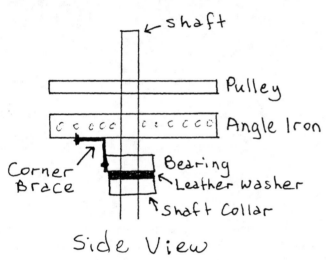

Side View

mounting holes, and bolted the other side of the braces to the flat steel. Murphy's Law insists that you will <u>always</u> have to drill new holes, no matter how many holes are already there to begin with.

This photo was taken before I rediscovered the principle of physics that states that "for every action, there is an equal and opposite reaction." In other words: the blade, which is pushing the slurry downward, will propeller itself right out of the mixer unless you attach a shaft collar to prevent it from rising. After I discovered this, I had to reattach the bearing <u>under</u> the flat steel, not above it, so that the shaft collar could push evenly against the bearing. Got that? Hopefully, the diagram will explain the situation more clearly. The photo shows how the bearing is attached to the flat steel with corner braces. The final configuration is exactly the same, only the bearing, and the braces, are below the flat steel rather than above it. Whew. No wonder they say that "a picture is worth a thousand words."

Between the shaft collar and the bearing, I put an oil-soaked 1" leather washer, which came with the shaft collar. I don't know if this has any effect, but it seemed the right thing to do.

Now it's really starting to look like a mixer. Let's look at a few details, starting from the bottom. First, the blade is rather far from the bottom of the tank, it seems to me. The diagram in Mike's book specified a 4" nipple attached to the flange, which is what I used, but it seems to me that a 2" nipple would work just fine, and the blade could then be 2" closer to the bottom of the tank.

Next, notice the curve in the blade. The blade turns counterclockwise, and the curve behind the cutting edge forces the slurry downward.

The motor has a 2" pulley on it, and the blade shaft has a 14" evaporative cooler pulley. With a 2-hp motor, you could probably use a 12" or even a 10" pulley on the blade shaft, which would give you a higher blade rpm. The set screw that comes with the pulley is <u>not</u> adequate to hold it onto the shaft. Instead, drill a 1/4" hole through the pulley, all the way through the shaft, and out the other side of the pulley. Then insert a 1/4" bolt and tighten it down.

Notice that the motor is mounted right next to the tank, with the shaft pointing up. This is the worst possible position for an electric motor. **It is important to completely shield the motor from rain, water, and slurry splashing.** Even though the motor is sealed, the cement and sand in the slurry are very abrasive, and will quickly destroy the seal. The cement and sand will then enter the motor and destroy the bearings.

With my setup, I cut slots into the angle iron where the motor is mounted, so that I could slide the motor along the slots and tighten the belt. With other motor mounting designs, another way of tightening the belt would have to be devised. ·

A BAFFLING SOLUTION

Mike's mixers are so high-powered that the slurry will spin around the tank at the same speed as the blade, which makes for inefficient mixing. He recommends adding a baffle to the inside of the tank. This introduces turbulence to the flow, greatly enhancing the cutting action of the blade.

I'm not sure if a baffle is required for such a low-powered mixer as mine, but I built one anyway. My baffle is simply a 2x4 screwed to the inside of the tank. I used rubber washers on the screws to prevent leaking.

PROTECTING THE MOTOR

This was my first attempt at protecting the motor. I used 1/2" foil-faced urethane foam insulation, pinned together with 6d nails and caulked along all the edges. This easily-constructed box is strong and waterproof. But it still wasn't enough—slurry would splash onto the v-belt, and would be carried into the box through the holes. It was finally necessary to install a horizontal splash guard across that entire side of the mixer, which was really no big deal.

Splashing is a normal part of the mixing process at the beginning of each mixing cycle, before the slurry gets thick. Look closely at the top two photographs on page 4 of EQ #1. Notice that Sean and Mike didn't cut the entire top off of Sean's mixer barrel—they cut a hole in the center, leaving a horizontal rim around the circumference of the barrel, which eliminates a lot of the splashing. Even so, notice the coating of dried slurry on the top and sides of the mixer barrel, and on the side of the pickup truck that powers his mixer. On page 7, notice all the dried slurry that had splashed onto the outside of Mike's tank.

I don't see splashing as a serious problem. It can be easily reduced to an acceptable level. Even when I first started out, and had no splash protection at all, I would lose maybe 1% of each load to splashing. Now, with a few simple splash guards in place, the splashing is very minimal.

USING THE MIXER

At long last we come to the payoff—using the darned thing. First, I fill the tank about half-full of water. This is about 70 gallons or so—the exact amount isn't critical. Then I dump in 4 shovels of cement. I started out using 3 shovels per batch, but when I realized how much wall I was building with so little cement, I decided to splurge with that extra shovel of cement per load. This, I figured, would give me a somewhat harder and stronger wall with only a slight increase in cost.

Notice the vertical splash guard made of pieces of corrugated fiberglass I had laying around. This simple splash guard can be inserted or removed in a matter of seconds.

All photos in this series are by Laura Solberg.

Next I add six shovels of sand harvested from a nearby arroyo. I screen the sand through a piece of 1/2" hardware cloth to remove the larger rocks. I add the cement and sand first to make sure that they are thoroughly mixed into the slurry. With my underpowered, low rpm mixer, I discovered that if I added the sand and cement at the end of the mixing cycle, they wouldn't be evenly mixed into the slurry.

This photo gives a good view of the horizontal splash guard I designed for the motor end of the mixer. It's made from a scrap piece of flat fiberglass, and remains permanently in place.

Then I add pre-soaked newspapers. I tear them in half and add them quickly, but one at a time. If I add too many newspapers at once, they bunch up on the leading edge of the blade, causing a tidal wave of slurry. It took only a few loads before Laura and I had figured out our mixing system. With the blade turning at only 200 rpm or so, with only a 1-hp motor powering it, we have found that the mixer works very well as long as we don't feed it too quickly. The best slurry fodder, we have found, is newspapers, magazines, and (hurrah!) junk mail. Paper bags, which have extra-strong fibers, don't work well for us, nor do cardboard boxes. Fortunately, we have access to a limitless supply of newspapers, magazines, and junk mail.

Towards the end of the mixing cycle, when the slurry thickens up and no longer splashes, we take off the splash guard and do a little "stick work" to make sure than no wads of newspaper are lurking in the corners of the tank. Laura is especially good at this. We stop the motor once or twice so that we can reach in and pull off any hunks of newspaper that are hung up on the leading edge of the blade. This would probably be less of a problem with a higher-powered mixer. Eric Patterson's self-cleaning s-blade design would be the best solution of all.

When is the slurry ready? This is hard to put into words. What, after all, is the difference between soupy goopy and sloppy gloppy? In the final analysis, it really doesn't matter all that much—the excess water drains, crystal clear, out of the slurry, leaving the cement and sand behind. We just keep adding paper until the slurry seems about right. No matter how thick you make the slurry, it will always contain a lot of loose water that will drain right out. And if the slurry is on the thin side, it's amazing how well it holds together anyway—if you shovel it out of the tank, it will stay in the shovel, whereas concrete made to the same soupy consistency would flow right out of the shovel. The point I am making here is that slurry is a very forgiving substance. After a very few loads you will learn to "eyeball" the right consistency, just like we did.

Early in our mixing career we simply scooped out the finished slurry—90-100 gallons per batch—with buckets. This isn't as bad as it sounds—paper slurry is much less heavy than concrete. I had originally wanted to pump the slurry out, but was unable to find the make and model # of a pump that was guaranteed to work for this application, and I was unwilling to risk $200+ on an unproved pump. I felt like I was guinea pig enough already.

In the background is a form for making 8x8x16" blocks.

Eventually I built a 2-foot-high platform for the mixer, cut a hole in the bottom of the tank for a 4" pvc outlet, and constructed a simple draining trough made of corrugated steel roofing. On top of the roofing metal is a piece of ½" hardware cloth covered with window screen. Pre-draining our slurry reduces settling in the forms, eliminates possible slurry water contamination of the work site, and allows us to recycle our slurry water.

Earth Quarterly's Paper Office

This summer, Laura and I completed about half the walls for our **Earth Quarterly** office—which is pretty good, considering that we were able to mix only five or so mixer loads a week. We poured the slurry directly into forms, eliminating the block-making process entirely. The wooden framework on the center wall is the result of a staff compromise—the editor wanted a solid papercrete center wall, while the publisher wanted no wall at all. So we compromised with a wall that's solid on the bottom, with an open wooden framework (for enhanced light and openness) at the top. I have already written a 4-page article on this building project, but there was no room for it in this issue. We hope to complete our office by the end of the year—knock on wood... I mean, knock on papercrete.

A HEAT TRANSFER EXPERIMENT WITH PAPERCRETE

In 1993 two students at New Mexico State University performed a heat transfer experiment as part of their course work. One material they tested was papercrete supplied by Eric Patterson. Eric sent us the following report, which we are printing in its entirety, exactly as we received it. We are printing the references to papercrete in bold type, to make them easier to find.

Date: May 12, 1993
To: Dr. Burchett
From: Tom Kehl and Ken Potter
Subject: Wall Heat Transfer Experiment

Table 1. Temperature Data

Wall Number	Description	Outside Wall Temperature (C)		
		0 hours	12 hours	36 hours
1	no insulation	24.5	26.9	28.2
2	5.5" fiberglass	24.9	26.0	27.3
3	3.5" cotton	25.2	26.2	27.3
4	**12" paper brick**	**24.4**	**25.3**	**26.8**
5	8" log	24.4	25.6	27.4
6	3.5" fiberglass	24.8	26.7	28.0

PURPOSE OF EXPERIMENT

The purpose of the experiment was to compare the insulating properties of six different wall constructions. An empty 2x4 stud wall was used as a reference for comparison.

SUMMARY OF RESULTS

Table 1. shows the temperature data for each of the six walls before the heater was turned on, twelve hours later, and at steady state, thirty-six hours.

EXPERIMENTAL APPARATUS

The experimental setup consisted of a six sided building. Each wall was constructed of a different material and measured four square feet. The description of each wall is shown in Table 1. The top and bottom of the structure were insulated with three sheets of one inch Styrofoam insulation to minimize heat loss through these surfaces. The building was heated internally by a 100 Watt light bulb. A fan was used to circulate the air inside the structure.

Temperature data was recorded from the K type thermocouples attached to the inside and outside of each wall. Equipment problems with the HP Data Acquisition Unit made this data unusable. We also recorded data with a *Probeye* infrared camera. This camera produced color coded temperature distributions of each wall and numerical values for the temperatures at the center of each wall. Pictures of the temperature distributions were taken at zero, one, two, three, four, eight, twelve, twenty, twenty-eight, and thirty-six hours after the heater was turned on. We used the camera to look at temperatures in the range of 20 C to 32.8 C. For this temperature range, the manufacturer claims a sensitivity of 0.1 C. However, we observed fluctuations in the center temperature of ±0.3 C.

DISCUSSION OF RESULTS

We used the outside wall temperature to compare the insulating properties of each wall. The greater the outside wall temperature, the greater the heat transfer through the wall. Therefore a cooler wall is better insulated. When comparing the insulating properties of building materials, the thermal mass should also be considered. A large thermal mall has a stabilizing effect on the inside temperature. Table 1 presents the temperatures at the center of the walls at times zero, twelve, and thirty-six hours after the heater was turned on.

The infrared pictures are identified by the wall number and time labels at the bottom of each picture. Wall 1 was the worst insulator since the outside temperature rose the fastest. The studs can be seen in the infrared picture of wall one at thirty-six hours. They appear slightly cooler than the rest of the wall. **The paper brick wall (4) was the best insulator. This can be attributed to the large thickness of the wall, twelve inches, and the high thermal mass.** Wall 5, the log wall, also produced good results. After twelve hours, the outside temperature was only slightly higher than the brick wall. After thirty-six hours the log wall was about the same temperature as the wall containing 5.5" of fiberglass insulation. The individual logs can be seen in the pictures. We believe this is due to the curvature of the logs. Light from the overhead lights reflected off the tops of the logs and to the camera. We were surprised to learn that the 3.5" fiberglass insulation was only marginally better than the empty wall. At both twelve and thirty-six hours, the insulated wall was only a few tenths of a degree cooler. However, the 5.5" fiberglass insulation performed better than the log wall at thirty-six hours but not as well at twelve hours. This is due to the difference in thermal masses of the log wall and the 5.5" insulation. The cotton wall (3) performed nearly identical to the 5.5" fiberglass insulation. However, the cotton wall was only 3.5" thick, therefore it is the better insulator.

RECOMMENDATIONS

We feel several changes to the experimental setup would improve the accuracy of the results. First, a larger heat source should be used to achieve a larger temperature difference between the inside and outside ambient temperatures. Therefore, differences in the insulating properties of each wall would be more apparent. Second, the experiment should be run in a better controlled environment. The ambient room temperature fluctuated constantly over the thirty-six hours that the experiment was run. Cool air from the air conditioner and radiation from the sun may have influenced our results. The reference temperature in the HP Data Acquisition Unit drifted upward over the course of the experiment and made the data unusable. This problem needs to be corrected.

Ideally, this experiment would be repeated using the improved procedures the authors recommend. However, the fact that the papercrete outperformed every other material, including 5.5" of fiberglass, is highly indicative of papercrete's outstanding insulating value.

UP IN SMOKE

On July 23 I had the following e-mail exchange with Paul Salas of Albuquerque, NM:

Have you tried any ignition tests on fibrous cement?

I had mixed a batch that made 5 gallons (3 lb paper, 1.5 lb sand and .5 lb cement) and poured it over wire mesh to dry (mostly drain). It was about 3" thick 10" wide and 16" long. It had been drying for about 4 days just outside our shop. I was welding on some equipment and a hot piece of slag landed on the material. Initially it just smoldered, no flame—the dark burn spot just got bigger—still no flames. It didn't smoke much, just felt hot like charcoal on a spit.

The gist of this is that I monitored this "cook-off" for about an hour and the burn area had spread into a 6" diameter and was burning very hot without any visible flame. I left it and let it burn itself out overnight. The next day, all had been consumed—every bit of it—and all that was left was about a 1/2 cup of ash residue.

I feel there is potential in this material just as you do; however, this unscientific "ignition test" says a lot about what would happen in a real house fire—total consumption.

Any thoughts or comments??????

That's an interesting observation! What impresses me is that it had only dried for 4 days, which isn't long for f.c. Was the paper totally ground up to an oatmeal-like consistency, or were there still pieces of paper in the slurry? This might have made a difference.

My own test was with a propane torch—I torched one spot for several minutes. It turned black and powdery where the flame hit it, but there was no independent combustion. I figured that if you had a house with a lot of flammable contents that burned, you would ruin your f.c. walls, but that the walls themselves wouldn't contribute to the fire. But your experience suggests otherwise.

I'd like to print your experience in EQ if this is OK with you. I think it's an important piece of information. I want to discuss the cons as well as the pros of f.c. I

think f.c. has a lot of potential, but I don't want to hype it at the expense of the truth, whatever that may be.

You can reprint or publish as you wish—observations and facts are what they are!!!

For mixing, I used a 1/2 HP two bladed chopper/mixer to puree the paper. I added only small amounts of newspaper to the mix to ensure that I got the material totally pulped. I ran my hands into the material to ensure that there were no pieces of paper still intact. I mixed the paper first in 14 liters of water, then added the cement, mixed it well, then added the sand in small portions to ensure that there was an even distribution within the mix. I observed no separation within the mix when I poured it out to dry.

During the time of this "experiment," the daytime temps were in the 105-107° range and in the high 80s in the evening. The first two days, the material seemed wet to the touch and spongy; however, by the evening of the third day there was a noticeable difference in the appearance of the material: dry and firm to the touch. The flame test I spoke of took place late on the 4th day about 7:00 p.m. We were just getting ready to go home when a friend of mine noticed that the "test piece" was smoking and had a burn spot on it. What actually fell on it was a piece of molten metal from cutting a piece of steel. Temp had to be in the 1400° range and stayed hot for quite a while. Everything stopped and it was time for observation—as noted earlier. The test piece may not have actually been totally dry and as the surface area ignited, the heat generated dried the adjacent areas sufficient to sustain ignition—possible explanation for the v e r y s l o w burn.

An interesting thing about the burn was that no "red" was observed unless the surface area was disturbed (wire welding rod) or by fanning the dark black burn area. Whenever any of the above were executed, it appeared that the cement or sand particles were being melted or transformed in some way because the particles were easily observed and glowed much brighter than the rest of the material. It was as though you could almost count the individual particles. Another interesting aspect was that there were passages or air pockets below the surface because small individual random black burn spots appeared within one to two inches away from the initial ignition area. After a while these would all combine into one larger burn area and the process would repeat itself. The burn area was initially very shallow and took a considerable amount of time to achieve the 3" depth of

the material. I still wonder what became of the sand and cement????

I was interested in FC as a supplement insulator to conventional adobe to meet minimum R-Value requirements for adobe construction. Unless I can modify the ignition problem, I may have to look elsewhere for insulation value.

This experience indicates that there's still a <u>lot</u> that we don't know about fibrous cement, and that there is much testing yet to be done. Perhaps there is a nontoxic fire retardant that could be added to the slurry?

Some Perspectives on Fibrous Cement/Papercrete

RECAP

Last issue we talked about **fibrous cement**, a remarkable building material made of old newspapers and magazines, sand, and cement. The raw ingredients are mixed together with water, creating a slurry that can be made into bricks, poured into forms, or used as plaster. After it dries, fibrous cement is lightweight, highly insulating (R 2.8 per inch), and very strong (it has both tensile and compressive strength). Since all the ingredients except for the cement can be obtained for free or almost free, fibrous cement is amazingly inexpensive—the cheapest price we know of so far is 39¢ per square foot for a basic, no-frills dome.

TERMINOLOGY

When I put together Issue 1 of **Earth Quarterly**, I had only heard the term, "fibrous cement," which can be made with any kind of fiber—sawdust, paper, straw, even dried weeds. It was only later that I was exposed to the term, "**papercrete**," which, technically speaking, is fibrous cement using paper as the fiber. To my way of thinking, "papercrete" has a more user-friendly, less "techno" sound than "fibrous cement," so that's what I'm calling it these days. But please, by all means, call it whatever you want.

REACTIONS

As you can see from our "Letters" section, we got a lot of enthusiastic feedback to our "Paper House" issue. (And this is only the response that was aimed in our direction—Issue 1 was photocopied by numerous people and passed from hand to hand, and there was also a fair amount of Internet "buzz.")

Some people asked me (referring to the 75¢ a square foot figure on the front cover) if that was a typo. Others asked me if I had dropped a decimal point somewhere along the line. Others had various concerns that I will address later in this article. But most of the feedback we received was overwhelmingly positive.

Whatever the pros and cons of papercrete may be, there's one thing I like about it a lot—and that's the science fiction quality of people building their homes from the detritus of a decadent and life-destroying civilization. This really appeals to me. For me, "Getting out from under the Global Exploitation Economy" conjures up images of tiny mammals scurrying around trying to avoid the lumbering (and soon to be extinct) dinosaurs that tower overhead. Under these circumstances, it makes a lot of sense to build a snug little shelter in an out-of-the-way spot—that way, we'll be as safe as possible when the dinosaurs start crashing down all around us.

RESEARCH IS NEEDED

This is an exciting time to be a papercrete builder—new techniques are being discovered all the time, and lots of mistakes are still being made. In a world dominated by a mainstream culture that has become sterile and over-programmed, it's good to know that it's still possible to be a pioneer.

Papercrete is so new that there hasn't even been a Paper Building Conference yet, though there probably will be before long. When that happens, papercrete pioneers will have the opportunity to share their mistakes as well as their triumphs, so that later generations of papercrete builders can avoid making the same errors, and can build upon the successful foundation the pioneers have already laid down.

There's a lot a research that needs to be done on papercrete, and this will require a certain amount of money. (But just think—for the cost of a single "stealth" bomber, we could fund all the research projects that every EQ reader could possibly conceive of. The money is already there—it's just being controlled by the wrong people.)

For starters, it would be good to pin down the compressive and tensile strength of papercrete under every possible moisture regime—when it's bone dry, after it has absorbed all the moisture it can from a 100% humidity atmosphere, when it's totally soaked, and when it contains different percentages of water. My guess is that its compressive strength would decrease gradually with increasing moisture content, while the tensile strength would decrease dramatically as you added water.

Another research project would be to repeatedly soak and dry out papercrete, and to see when, if at all, it starts to break down.

It would be valuable to test the water that drains out of the slurry. This water is crystal clear, but there's no telling what might be dissolved in it. It would be instructive to compare the slurry water made from different types of paper, and different types of inks.

Another project would be to determine the thermal characteristics of papercrete with different proportions of sand added to the mix. Start with a basic R value test. Then run tests to determine how quickly heat flows through papercrete under different temperature regimes, and how well the addition of sand creates a "thermal flywheel effect," as detailed in our last issue.

(I must confess to some inaccurate terminology last issue on page 3, at the top of column two. When speaking about substances that have a high insulating and a high thermal mass all in one package, I should have said, "Few building materials can make this claim.") What's intriguing about papercrete with sand added is that here we have individual grains of sand separated rather widely within an insulating matrix, so that it takes a relatively long time for heat to flow from one sand grain to the next. This is an intuitively fascinating concept, but considerable laboratory testing would be required (using different concentrations of sand) before we could get a clear idea about the advantages, if any, to adding sand to the mix for this purpose.

CONCERNS

Various people have expressed some concerns about papercrete that I would like to discuss here:

CEMENT. As traditionally formulated, papercrete contains cement. There is no doubt that cement is an energy intensive product. Not only does it take a lot of fossil fuels to heat up the raw materials (mostly limestone, clay and sand, with smaller amounts of aluminum, iron and gypsum) to 2700°, but cement production creates a "double whammy" of CO_2, because the purpose of all that heat is to drive off the CO_2 from the limestone (calcium carbonate, $CaCO_3$) to turn it into lime (calcium oxide, CaO). One estimate I read says that every pound of cement produced puts a pound of CO_2 into the atmosphere. Then, of course, the heavy bags of cement have to be trucked from the factory to the building site, dumping yet more CO_2 into the atmosphere. However, when the cement is mixed with water, sand, and gravel to make concrete (or with water, sand, and paper to make papercrete), CO_2 is absorbed from the atmosphere back into the concrete (or papercrete) as it dries. One person estimates that under some circumstances, 80% of the CO_2 created by the manufacturing process is reabsorbed back into the concrete as it dries. This is a complicated issue, and as usual I don't think we have all the necessary information to understand the situation like we really need to.

(Some people use lime as a cement substitute, believing lime to be a more ecologically benign substance than cement. However, lime is manufactured by heating limestone to drive off the CO_2—in fact, portland cement is 60-67% lime by weight. If a person chooses not to use cement because of its environmental impacts, then lime doesn't seem like much of alternative.)

Cement production is the third-largest source of human-made CO_2 emissions, accounting for 2½% of the total. Deforestation is #2. The primary source, accounting for a whopping 80% of human CO_2 production, is the burning of fossil fuels.

I think it's important to keep the "cement issue" in perspective. Of course it's important to keep our environmental impacts to a minimum, but it's obvious that the relatively small amount of cement each of us uses in a lifetime is but a tiny fraction of the environmental damage caused by our fossil fuel habit (either directly, as when we drive automobiles or fly in jet airliners, or indirectly, as when we eat food that has been transported halfway across the country (or, as is increasingly common in this bold new era, halfway around the world)).

Each gallon of gasoline we burn releases nearly 20 pounds of CO_2 into the atmosphere. Driving a car that gets 25 mpg 15,000 miles a year produces 12,000 pounds of CO_2. This is the CO_2 equivalent of 128 bags of cement, not taking into account the CO_2 reabsorbed when the cement is turned into concrete, or the other toxins—carbon monoxide, hydrocarbons, nitrogen oxide, and other noxious substances—spewed from the tailpipes of our cars. Happy driving!

MOISTURE. Although papercrete absorbs water like a sponge, there should not be a moisture problem if a papercrete structure is built on top of a concrete foundation with a moisture barrier to prevent wicking, and if it is painted on the outside with silicone sealer or some other substance that will prevent water from penetrating from the outside. Various moisture control strategies are discussed elsewhere in this issue.

Papercrete slurry is notorious for drying very slowly. The biggest moisture problem, I think, would be getting the slurry to dry out in the first place in a cool and humid climate. But almost any climate will have relatively warm, dry periods. So it's important to choose your construction time carefully. Also, in wet climates it would be important to cover the work in progress with tarps or plastic during rainy weather.

My experience building with forms indicates that forms would not be the way to go in a cool, moist climate. Every time you raise your form to the next level and pour wet slurry into it, the excess water saturates the previously-constructed wall. Not until the final form is filled at the very top will the wall start to dry—very slowly—from the top down.

Best in a moist climate would be to build with blocks—they could be constructed long in advance, so they would have plenty of time to dry, and could be stored in a shed or under a tarp. Then, during the driest time of the year, the entire structure could be built very rapidly using the stored blocks. The minimal amount of mortar needed to stick the blocks together would not soak the blocks, and would dry relatively quickly. A roof could be built within a matter of days, and the outside of the blocks could be plastered and painted with silicone sealer. Getting all this done between rains, and covering the partially-completed structure with tarps if rains do come, is the key. After you get the roof on and the outside sealed, the blocks can finish drying from the outside in. One EQ reader suggested putting a wood heater inside the structure and keeping it burning until the wall finishes drying, at which time the inside of the structure could be sealed as well.

One important piece of research that needs to be done is: how much moisture will dry blocks absorb from the air in a humid climate, and will this moisture compromise the longevity or the structural integrity of the blocks?

People who intend to build with papercrete in a humid environment should view dryness as a precious investment that needs to be protected at all times by dry foundations, moisture barriers, silicone sealer, and roofs with substantial overhangs.

FIRE. As the article "Up in Smoke" indicates, papercrete evidently will burn, though very slowly. Research needs to be done to thoroughly explore this area. Until that time, perhaps papercrete should be promoted as "semi-fireproof." By no means is papercrete as flammable as ordinary lumber, and this is a key fact. Millions of wood frame homes are considered safe enough to qualify for fire insurance. Since papercrete burns much less rapidly than wood, I don't see how there can be too much concern about its flammability.

WIND. Since a papercrete structure has a pressure of only one pound per square inch on the foundation, most people I have spoken to agree that it would be a very good idea to make sure that the building is tightly anchored to a heavy foundation. This would be especially true for a rectangular building with a conventional overhanging roof. A good method would be to borrow a straw bale building technique and embed steel strapping into the foundation, and run it over the roof plates. This would anchor both the roof and the walls to the foundation.

LOOSE ENDS

Last issue I neglected to mention how Mike sealed his mixer where the car drive shaft penetrates the bottom of the stock tank. The answer is: he didn't. There was some leaking the first time the mixer was used, but the slurry filled any gaps, preventing subsequent leaking.

Another fact I should have mentioned is that Sean's house has an underground ventilation pipe which brings in a constant supply of fresh air from outside. Since the air pipe is underground, the air is automatically warmed during the winter and cooled during the summer.

Sean's method of making "sandbag blocks" might seem like a lot of unnecessary work, but has the advantage of draining the slurry three times: (1)immediately after leaving the mixer, (2)when it is put into the sandbags in the vertical stovepipes, and (3)when he lays the sandbags into the forms and tamps them with a hoe. This definitely makes for a denser, stronger, more uniform block. I mentioned this in passing in my article, but after having worked with slurry for awhile, I want to re-emphasize how important proper draining really is.

BUILDING THE CHEAPEST STRUCTURE POSSIBLE

Sean Sands is doing valuable work, finding out just how cheaply a structure can be built. His domes are especially innovative—using papercrete blocks made with his dome form, a dome can be quickly and easily built for the remarkably low materials cost of 39¢ a square foot. But it is possible to lower the cost even more.

The way to do this would be to make the blocks out of paper and clay, with no cement added. There would be no "bought" materials whatsoever. After such a structure

(Continued on page 100)

Building with Paper Bales

Mary Hardin

PAPER BALES

Imagine the amount of waste paper generated by a university with 35,000 students. Much of that paper is recyclable, but there are still tons of paper that go into landfills each year. Glossy magazine stock, paper with fluorescent colors, wrappers for the reams of copy paper, chipboard, etc. are not acceptable at many recycling centers. In partnership with the University of Arizona, a Tucson company (Resource Recycling Service) took a step to discover solutions to this growing dilemma by experimenting with the production of shredded paper bales. By shredding mixed paper to achieve uniform consistency, compressing it in a baler, and banding it with 1/2" steel bands, the Resource Recycling Service developed the ECO-BALE.

Initial testing showed the bales to be stronger under a compressive load than straw bales, with a lesser insulating value (estimated thermal resistance of R-30) due to greater mass and density. Like straw bales, the paper bales performed well in fire tests because their compression left little oxygen within the bales to aid in combustion. The production of paper bales makes sense in a desert setting where straw is not normally cultivated and has to be trucked in from other parts of the state or country. The Resource Recycling Service saw the paper bales as a potential material for housing construction, either as a loadbearing system or as infill walls in a post and beam system.

A PAPER BALE PROJECT

In the Spring semester of 1998, a team of Architecture students at the University of Arizona set out to build an experimental structure of shredded paper bales, in an endeavor to reroute the non-recyclable material that is otherwise headed for landfills. Jean Nielsen, the coordinator of campus organization Arizona Resource Exchange (AzRE), contacted Professor Mary Hardin and her students with a unique challenge: to design and construct a building with 150 ECO-BALES.

Architecture graduate student Obadiah Swafford took on the project as part of his Master's thesis and coordinated the materials lists, tool gathering, and construction labor schedule. Professor Hardin suggested a construction strategy based on her previous experience with load bearing straw bales. Graduate students Lance Lewis and Siobhan Kirby, as well as undergraduates Jeffrey Lavy and Richard Begay, joined the team for independent study credit, and work commenced.

With the cooperation of the College of Agriculture, the Architecture team created a floor plan and a construction strategy for a storage building that would house a tractor and other equipment needed for honey bee research. The structure covers an area of 1000 square feet—600 square feet are enclosed and an additional 400 square feet are defined by walls and an overhead shade structure.

The entire project is built of salvaged, donated, and recycled materials, with a budget of $0.00. Design decisions were modified weekly in response to available materials and tools. Many choices of materials and methods were compromises. While this may be a frustrating way to build, it does bring out creativity and cause debate (rewards in themselves in the educational setting).

The initial step in the construction was to trench for footings that would support the bale walls. The paper bales measure 48" long by 24" wide and 18-20" high. The trenches were dug 24" wide and 18" deep by the University Grounds crew, who donated their time and backhoe. The formwork was borrowed from a local concrete company, and used to define the top 4 inches of the footings, which were to remain above grade.

In the photographs, rows of bottles are visible along the outside of the formwork. These were placed against the forms and covered with dirt in order to create a dam to hold back concrete during the pour (an ad hoc invention that worked remarkably well!).

While the concrete was wet, anchor bolts were placed along the edges of the footings, to receive the pressure-treated lumber that would raise the paper bales off the concrete for moisture protection. A row of rebar spikes was cast down the middle of the footings to impale the first course of paper bales.

The bottoms of the trenches were filled with pea gravel to a depth of 9 inches. Rebar cages were placed in the forms and the remaining 9 inches was filled with the tail end of a concrete pour, donated by a local contractor. In this photograph, graduate student Siobhan Kirby is guiding the concrete pour.

The walls of the main storage area are supported by these fairly traditional footings. The ramada walls, however, are supported by more experimental means. The trench for one wall was filled with glass cullet, created by smashing glass bottles found on the site, topped with concrete.

The trench for the other ramada wall was completely filled by bales of compressed plastic soda bottles, wired together for transport to a landfill. The plastic bales were set in the trench, leaving about 2 feet of the bales exposed above ground. The paper bale walls were constructed right on top of the plastic bale foundation. Here you see Obi Swafford shoveling dirt into the trenches around the plastic bales. Time and measurements will allow comparison of the settling of the various wall systems.

The final step in preparing the footings was to bolt down pressure treated 2x4s and "Liquid Nail" a piece of flashing along the outside edge of the footing to serve as a termite shield. The developers of the ECO-BALES assert that termites will not be attracted to the paper, because during the pulping process most of the nutrient value is lost. However, Tucson dwellers know from experience that termites will bore through stacks of paper (perhaps in search of wood) and the project will receive termite treatment.

Once the footings were prepared, the bale construction began in the manner of loadbearing straw bales. But because the paper bales are so heavy (275 pounds each), the rolling and lifting soon became exhausting. This is a definite drawback to the system—the work is slower and the upper courses require real coordination for safety. The first course of bales was placed quickly by rolling them to their location and lifting them onto the footings. Jumping on the bales pushed them down onto the rebar spikes and held them in place. In this illustration, Obi Swafford and Mary Hardin take turns impaling the bales.

45

The second course went up quickly as well, and it began to look as if the wall raising might be completed in just a few hours. But, the next step—tying the courses together vertically, proved to be a real struggle. The plan was to hammer long rebar spikes down through each bale; to pin it to the course or two below it. But, the many directions of the dense shredded paper made each bale almost impossible to penetrate, even using a sledge hammer.

By the third course of bales, a forklift was borrowed to transport the bales, and the system of joining the paper bales had been modified. Using a rebar bender, the rebar spikes were converted to staples and driven into each pair of adjacent bales, thus joining each course horizontally. In this photograph, Jeffrey Lavy mass-produces rebar staples.

So, grade stakes were sharpened and pounded in to create guide holes, then pulled out and rebar spikes were driven in. This labor was very slow, and demanded full effort. Here the paper bale team takes a break on the walls.

After that, 12 gauge fence wire was used to vertically weave together the steel straps that bound the bales; creating a sort of net of bales, wire and staples. The team's idea is that the net will cause the walls to act monolithically under stress rather than moving individually within the wall.

Once the fifth and final course was in place, the walls were braced and covered with tarps (actually recycled circus tents) to protect them from rain. To create a roof assembly that would give lateral stability to the bale walls and provide a nailing surface for rafters, the team designed a continuous collar beam that went around the top of the walls. It was made of parallel 2x10s set on edge , with a "lid" of OSB (oriented strand board) nailed to the top edges and 2x4 blocking inside.

This made a stiff member as wide as the bales, that spanned door and window openings. The Architecture team noticed that the collar beam immediately pulled the walls together and stiffened up the whole building. Although it is difficult to see in the photographs, the collar beam is pinned down into the bales. Before the lid was nailed on, holes were drilled through blocking members and rebar pins were driven down through the 2x4s into the bales until a 90-degree bend at the top stopped their progress.

The team also had a strategy for making a continuous connection between the foundation and the roof. They ran pallet strapping under the pressure treated floor plates before anchoring them down and filling in between them with pea gravel. After the walls were up and the collar beam was in place, the pallet straps were pulled up one side of a wall, over the collar beam, and back down the other side of the wall to meet the piece sticking out from under the floor plates. Each strap was cinched tightly to form a loop that connected the entire wall from foundation to roof. Here Siobhan cinches straps to complete the loop.

After this point, the rest of the construction was fairly conventional. Although a shed roof had been planned, it proved impossible to acquire the necessary 28' TJI joists* with no budget. Shorter 2x6 lumber was available, so the

47

team improvised a ridge beam out of salvaged flat trusses and framed a shallow gable roof.

*TJI is a trade name for "engineered lumber joists," which are like composite wooden I-beams. They have plywood or OSB webs and solid lumber flanges at the top and bottom. They are an inexpensive way to achieve a long span because they are stiff due to their shape, but are made of recycled wood. They are used for roofs and floors.

Windows were incorporated into spaces created by removing a bale. 2x6 frames provided a nailing surface for the nailing flanges of the aluminum windows. The frames were actually were hung from the collar beam, as it was easiest to nail them to another wooden member. An alternative would have been to drill holes in the sides of the window frames and drive wooden dowels or rebar pins through to the paper bales on either side of the frame.

Richard Begay attaches 2x6 joists to the ridge beam with joist hangers.

The gable ends were covered with strips of corrugated Kal-Wall, which let a soft yellow light into the interior of the shed. The roof is sheathed in OSB and then corrugated galvanized aluminum (picked out of an ancient pile on the site).

These overall views show the storage structure and ramada before they were wrapped for stucco application.

A door frame was built into the opening in the bale wall under the ramada. The 2x6 framing members were nailed into the wood floor plates and up into the collar beam. Then 2x4s were added within this larger frame until the rough opening was the correct size for hanging the door.

At this point, the rammed earth floor was tamped. Using a small garden rototiller, students mixed 27 parts earth (sand, clay, silt and gravel) with 1 part cement and enough water to achieve a proper consistency (one that allowed a ball of earth formed in the hand to remain in a ball when the fist is opened). This earth mixture was spread out on the interior floor surface to a depth of about 6 inches, then tamped with a "flapjack" to a final depth of 4 inches. In this photo, Obadiah Swafford drives the flapjack.

Preparation for stucco required four steps. The first was to cover all the wood that would eventually have stucco on it with black water resistant paper. The paper was stapled onto

the collar beam all the way around the building as well as around the door frame and beams atop the ramada walls. The second step was to nail metal strips called "J-stop" to the top and bottom edges of the bale walls, where the stucco would stop. These J-shaped strips turn outward to form an edge against which the thick layers of stucco can come to rest. The J-stop was nailed to the collar beam at the top of the walls, and to the wooden floor plates at the bottom. This was a real struggle, because the bales protruded unevenly, and had to be "trimmed" back with the claw of a hammer when the shredded paper obscured the nailing surfaces. Next, expanded metal lath was nailed on wherever there was a transition between two materials, in order to provide a uniform surface so that the stucco could bridge the gaps. For example, an 18 inch strip of expanded metal lath was nailed into the collar beam and then pegged into the paper bales below all the way around the structure. This makes a continuous, well textured surface so that the stucco won't crack between the collar beam and the walls. The metal lath was also used at all corners, inside and out, to ease the turns and let the stucco cling uniformly. 60-penny spikes were used to attach the lath to the bales. Galvanized 6-penny nails were used to attach lath to all wood surfaces. Finally, stucco netting (like chicken wire) was stretched from collar beam down to the wooden floor plates so that the entire wall surface was covered. Notice the four layers of preparatory materials in these views.

Rather than the sliding garage door that was part of the original plan, the College of Agriculture provided a gate made of galvanized steel tubes and chain link fence material. This was positioned on a steel frame in front of the door for the tractor, and pivots open on large hinges. A wheel supports the weight of the gate at the open end and allows it to roll with minimal effort.

The final step of the process is the stucco application. It will be sprayed on in three coats, and can be painted or left a natural grey-brown. Interior as well as exterior walls will be finished with stucco, due to the fact that weather can blow in through the garage door opening.

CONCLUSIONS

Some preliminary conclusions can be drawn about paper bale construction as the project nears completion. The construction method used by Professor Hardin's class resulted in design considerations and costs similar to straw bale construction. The structural walls are inexpensive while the other assemblies (foundations, roof, interior partition walls) are conventional in costs and techniques. However, the paper bales are heavier and more difficult to handle than straw bales. This drawback has to be weighed against issues of availability of straw and transportation costs if it has to be trucked in from a long distance.

The difficulties involved in pinning bales vertically and providing lateral stability to a wall of bales made Professor Hardin's team wary of using paper bales as loadbearing walls again. The insulation value of the bales makes them a good choice for infill walls in a post and beam structure. Obadiah Swafford and Professor Hardin proposed a post and beam structure on a 12 foot grid, with bales stacked in between. The dimensional stability of the post and beam structure would also alleviate worries about uneven settling of the bales, as the roof would not bear on the bales. The problems involved in pinning bales together would be avoided as well, and lateral stability of the walls could be provided by diagonal bracing from post to post.

The trials and tribulations of any new building system can only be learned by experimenting with it. The struggles with this paper bale structure have been worth the effort, even if the conclusions seem to lead away from the use of the bales as loadbearing units. Discoveries made along the way have revealed attributes of the paper bales that the class did not suspect. For example, the density of the bales makes them almost impervious to water. The structure stood roofed, but not yet plastered, through Tucson's summer monsoon season. The bales were hit repeatedly with driving rain from all directions, and yet never swelled. Bales opened after the rains revealed that water had penetrated only about 1/4 to 1/2 of an inch. Wet bales quickly dried out in the desert air, and seem to hold promise for use in emergency shelter, as well as use in long term, plastered structures.

MORE INFORMATION

Richard Harrell, co-owner of Resource Recycling Service of Tucson, has recently moved to Deming, New Mexico. The ECO-BALES are not currently being produced in Tucson. Harrell had planned to collect non-recyclable paper types in depositories located at grocery stores throughout the city, shred it to achieve uniform consistency, and bale it in a baler converted from an industry-standard paper baler. The minor modifications Harrell made to the baler were justified because the goal was to get a narrower bale and stack the bales flat in a load bearing system. If, however, bales were used as infill in a post and beam wall, they could be stacked on edge, and the industry standard bale (48x30x18) would be just fine.

The initiator of the this project, Jean Nielsen, works for the campus Recycling Center (520-621-1264) as coordinator of Arizona Resource Exchange.

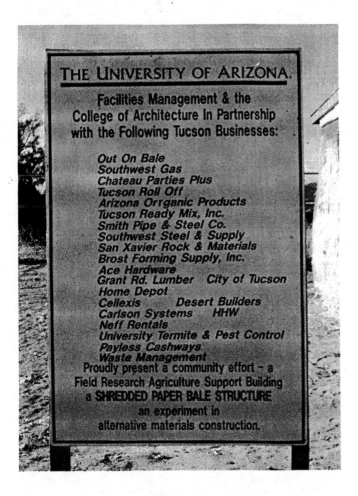

Professor Mary Hardin is a licensed architect who teaches full time in the College of Architecture at the University of Arizona and involves her students in design/build projects throughout the state of Arizona. Together they have built several concrete block houses and a straw bale house in the Yaqui community of Guadalupe, a rammed earth classroom in Tucson, and this paper bale structure. They are currently working on plans for rammed earth housing that will be built on the Gila Indian Reservation in 1999. She can be reached at the College of Architecture, University of Arizona, Tucson, AZ 85721 or mchardin@u.arizona.edu.

All photographs in this article are by Richard Begay, Jeffrey Lavy, and Mary Hardin.

The World's Oldest Papercrete Dome (that we know of)

The world's oldest papercrete dome that we know of was built in 1983-84 by James Moon of Tucson, Arizona. This is not his real name. James has long since moved on to other projects, and is no longer interested in talking to people about his dome. It was through the good graces of a mutual friend that James graciously gave Laura and me a tour of his dome this past October. He requested that we not use his real name, nor print his address.

The story of this dome begins back in 1980, when James was working on a construction project. After the day's work was done, they would throw the used cement bags into the mortar mixer, and run it awhile to clean it out Then they would dump the slurry onto the ground. James noticed that this slurry hardened into a substance that had intriguing properties—it was lightweight, yet held its shape and seemed quite strong. He thought it would make a good building material. James had independently discovered papercrete!

A couple of years later, he saw a macramé project in which circular macramé rings were interlocked to form a dome-shaped basket. What if he used this interlocking ring concept on a much larger scale to build a dome framework that would be lightweight, yet very strong? This framework could be covered with papercrete, and construction costs would be very low.

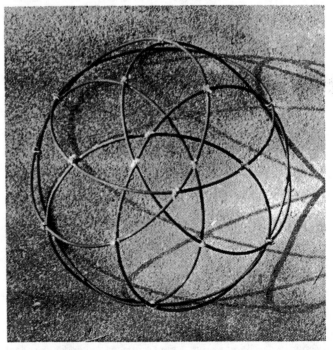

This photo shows a scale model of how the rings are combined to form a dome. The symmetry is elegant and beautiful. When he built his dome, he used ¾" electrical conduit and a conduit bender to construct six overlapping rings, which were bolted together wherever they crossed. The resulting framework was very strong. James says that you can squish the rings up or down to vary the shape of your dome, depending on how high you want your ceiling to be.

His dome is 12 feet in diameter and 9 feet tall, and weighs only 300 pounds. It was built on a wooden platform, which has been severely damaged by termites during the past 15 years. The dome itself, however, has not been damaged.

He covered the framework with 1x2" welded wire fabric to support the papercrete. He mixed his papercrete in a cement mixer, and used a 50/50 ratio of cement and paper (by weight). Mixing was the big bottleneck—he says that each load took 10 minutes to mix, but only 1 minute to apply to the wire fabric. The papercrete on this dome is 1" thick, has an estimated R-value of 4, and dried in 4 days. He sealed both sides of the papercrete with elastomeric roof coating ("Kool Kote"). The dome is remarkably tough. James kicked it—hard—to demonstrate its strength. The dome is much stronger than the human foot.

The dome took 40 hours to build, and cost less than $3 a square foot.

Here's another view of the dome, with a large cholla cactus in the foreground. James attached wooden window frames to the conduit before papercreting the dome.

James worked extensively on his dome ideas for three years. He had plans to build two-story domes up to 40 feet in

diameter, and to market dome kits, but in 1987 he moved on to other projects. We are pleased to have the opportunity to print his innovative ideas in **Earth Quarterly**. This article is just a teaser. Next issue, we'll be running a much longer article by James Moon, with step-by-step photos of how he built his dome.

PAPERCRETE Q & A

EQ reader Vince Konsavage of Jacksonville, FL sent us some papercrete questions. This seems to be as good a place as any to answer them:

Wet/cold locations—is it necessary to stucco or otherwise seal outer surfaces? What is effect of freezing?

Mike McCain's "snail house," built in Alamosa, CO, is a good example of how untreated papercrete withstands rain, snow, and extreme low temperatures (temperatures in Alamosa frequently fall below zero). This building has an underlined papercrete roof which shows no damage, and doesn't leak, after four cold, snowy, Colorado winters.

Another example is a house he built during the fall of 1997. The papercrete was still wet when cold temperatures hit, and the roof froze solid and remained that way throughout the winter of 1997-98, despite the efforts of the inhabitants to thaw it out by building large fires in the wood heater inside. Come the spring thaw, the roof was evidently undamaged.

We received an e-mail from Mark Piepkorn which is relevant here: *"Going through the July/August 97 back issue of Environmental Building News I came across an article on siding which includes a page on fiber-cement materials (Portland cement, sand, wood fiber, clay). An extremely different use than EQ has been reporting on, but you might want to pass along the reference. A caution from the article: 'Moisture absorption and subsequent freeze-thaw conditions have proved to be a problem with fiber-cement roofing shingles in cold climates.'"*

Several people are using papercrete as an unsealed, breathable, insulating exterior coating. However, an industrial designer we spoke to says that his experiments show that papercrete starts to break down after 50 wet/dry cycles. All this goes to show that papercrete (at least at the grassroots level) is still experimental, and we won't know how all these real life experiments have turned out until several more years have passed.

Has anyone tried adding clay to the basic mud mix? How should the 60/30/10 formula be altered for clay?

There are several people experimenting with using no cement at all—just paper, clay, and sometimes straw (which helps prevent cracking). People are calling this "fibrous adobe" and "paper cob." Mike McCain recommends that, when using both cement and clay, to add the cement first so that it can bind with the paper fibers, then add the clay. As for ratios, it depends on your dirt. Make test bricks, and let them dry, before you go into major production. I suspect that the trend of the future will be to emphasize clay instead of cement—it's cheaper and a lot more sustainable. "Paper adobe" would have the advantages of low cost, as well as superior insulating value (plain dirt is a lousy insulator).

Has anyone tried adding styrofoam beads or peanuts to the mix in order to increase R-value and decrease weight?

Not that I know of, but it sounds feasible. I suspect that the most sustainable use of styrofoam packaging would be to reuse it indefinitely as packaging.

How about adding glass fibers to the mix (can be obtained cheaply from fiberglass fabricators—boats/auto parts/etc.—by asking that they run their "chopper" guns without resin into a large carton or plastic bag)?

I saw an experimenter who was chopping polypropylene rope into 1" segments and mixing these fibers into his papercrete. Any kind of long fibers (longer than the relatively short paper fibers) would increase the tensile strength. The cost-effectiveness would depend on how many glass fibers you would have to add to get a significant increase in tensile strength. It is possible that straw might be cheaper and more eco-friendly. As usual, much experimentation will be necessary before we can determine if additional fibers are necessary at all, and if so, what kind and how many would be optimal.

Recent Papercrete Innovations

I had planned on doing a couple of full-length papercrete articles, "A Colorado Papercrete Tour," and "A Papercrete Workshop at WindTree Ranch," but we simply don't have room in this issue, even though we have expanded to 56 pages. What I'll do here is select some of my favorite topics and write a little bit about each one.

I'd like to thank Mike McCain for sharing so freely of his time and expertise. He gave Laura and me a tour of his projects in Crestone, CO, on Sept. 22, and the next day he showed us two papercrete structures he had built in the Alamosa area. Hopefully next issue we'll have room to print a more thorough write-up of what he's been up to recently.

The big bugaboo with fibrous cement is the mixer. Since there is presently no one that we know of making blocks for sale, you've got to make your own, and this means building a mixer.

My experience with the electric mixer I built and described in

detail last issue is: it works fine, but it's frustratingly slow. There's got to be a better way! Fortunately, Mike has come up with a couple of better ways.

Mike has built a number of "tow mixers" or "drag mixers" (designed to be towed or dragged behind a vehicle) utilizing an automotive rear axle, and a 4-foot diameter stock tank. This view shows the underside of a tow mixer. Notice the welded steel support framework. This mixer design is a larger-capacity version of his "Third World Mixer," described in our first issue.

This top view shows a lawnmower blade attached to the driveshaft end of the axle assembly. He seals the holes in the bottom of the tank with Bondo, an automotive body filler. He prefers to use an 18" or larger blade.

> **"'Small is beautiful,' but big is powerful. As long as big is powerful, 'small is beautiful' won't work." —ecologist Eugene P. Odum**

When he demonstrated his tow mixer for us in Crestone, he first put in a heaping wheelbarrow load of dry magazines, an entire 94-pound bag of cement, and 3-4 5-gallon buckets of sandy dirt (the exact number of buckets is hidden somewhere within 6 hours of tapes we haven't transcribed yet). In this picture, Mike is adding water to the mixer.

This picture, taken from the back of the truck immediately after we got underway, shows the raw ingredients still in their unmixed state.

A block later, at 5 mph, the ingredients were already mixed into a slurry. You've got to see it to really believe it—literally one block up the street and one block back, and you've got 200 gallons of slurry ready to go. The tow mixer concept still needs a lot of fine tuning, and tow mixers don't always work the way they should. But when they do work, the production possibilities are impressive.

54

Here's how Mike does serious production. The tow mixer straddles this wooden form, and the slurry is emptied directly into the form. There's no shoveling of slurry or carrying it around in buckets. After the slurry has drained enough for the blocks to hold their shape, he uses a dolly to pry the form up off the blocks, and inserts a couple of motorcycle wheels into a piece of rebar at the end of the form.

Then he walks to the other end of the form, slips the dolly underneath, and rolls the form to its new location. Mike makes 26

blocks at a time (shown stacked up behind the form in the previous photo). Entrepreneurs take note: Mike estimates that one person working at a modest pace can make 50 blocks an hour this way. When we were promoting EQ in Flagstaff and Tucson, we had dozens of people ask us where they could buy papercrete blocks. So the market is already there for anybody who cares to tap into it.

What excites Mike most these days is his garbage disposal mixer. In this photo, he demonstrates a prototype version at the WindTree Ranch workshop. From the bottom up, the mixer consists of a 1/2 hp garbage disposal unit, a coffee can, and a length of stovepipe. Water is dribbled into the top as soaked newspaper is added, and presto!—instant paper pulp is ejected from the garbage disposal. This pulp can be used immediately, or can be dried and transported to the construction site, at which time it can be reconstituted by adding water.

Pulping the paper is the main bottleneck to making papercrete. Mixing in the other ingredients—cement, sand, and/or clay—once the paper is pulped is relatively simple, and can be done with an ordinary cement mixer, or by hand with a wheelbarrow and hoe.

He says that a 1/2 hp garbage disposal is just about right for a small home operation. He plans to experiment with high capacity, industrial-strength units in the future.

A small, inexpensive, garbage disposal mixer like this has the capability of transforming the papercrete movement from a fringe movement into a not-quite-so-fringe movement. No longer will it be necessary to build a large, unwieldy mixer. A garbage disposal mixer can create pulp as fast as you can add paper to it, and the final mixing can be done in a cement mixer, and cement mixers can be found just about anywhere.

That wraps up the live coverage for this issue. Like I said, I hope to have room next issue for lots more papercrete information. One final note: After we put out issue 1, we encountered a certain amount of skepticism about the "75¢ a square foot" figure we printed on our cover. So when we were in Crestone I asked Mike for his latest materials cost estimate for a completed papercrete house—walls, floor, and roof. His answer? "Less than $1.00 a square foot." But that's nothing—Sean Sands, who is now making "paper adobe" with no cement, has his estimated materials cost down to 14¢ a square foot! Unbelievable? Next issue will tell the tale.

PAPERCRETE PERSPECTIVES
Part 2

DISCLAIMER

If Mike McCain, who probably has more hands-on papercrete experience than anyone in the world (at least at the grassroots level) claims not to be a papercrete expert, then what does that make me? Not only am I not a papercrete expert, I don't want to be a papercrete expert! I enjoy putting out an inspiring and informative magazine, and hope that I am writing about papercrete (and many other things) in an effective and entertaining way. But I'm no papercrete expert. If I ever print any inaccurate information in these pages, please let me know and I'll make it right.

A LITTLE FABLE

Once upon a time, there were some inventors who constructed an airplane out of bubble gum and baling wire. This attracted a lot of attention. In fact, a magazine (which we shall call *Smurf Quarterly*) even did a special "Airplane Issue" about their invention. Inevitably, the plane crashed. People gathered around the wreckage. "This proves that airplanes can't fly!" said some. Others said, "We need stiffer bubble gum!" Others said, "No, it's the baling wire!" But just over the hill, unbeknownst to all, was a busy airport with jets taking off and landing once a minute.

PAPERCRETE IS EXPERIMENTAL!

Papercrete, also known as fibrous cement, is very much an experimental building technique at our grassroots, "bubble gum and baling wire" level. Many mistakes are still being made. This is an exciting time for papercrete innovators, because it's at the beginning, when mistakes are still being made, that the learning curve is steepest. If you are looking for tried-and-true building techniques, there is an enormous amount of information already out there. But if you're looking for exciting new developments in low-cost, owner-built housing, you've come to the right place.

BUILDING CODES

One of the most frequently asked questions we are asked about papercrete is, "What about building codes?" I suspect that Mike McCain's experience, as reported in issue 1, page 13, is not typical. Most building inspectors are going to be much more hard-nosed about papercrete. This was our experience when we talked to our local building inspector in Doña Ana County, NM. He said that papercrete would qualify for an "experimental permit," which requires an engineer signing off on a set of plans. This is expensive, but would probably be the most straightforward alternative for most people. It will take years of jumping through hoops before papercrete gets code approval. Hopefully somebody out there will start jumping before long.

Other possibilities would include the "outlaw option" for people who are inclined this way—just go ahead and do it (ideally in a secluded location). (We are not recommending this, of course!) Also, there are still many rural counties with either minimal codes, or minimal codes enforcement. Build your dream home now, and hopefully it will be grandfathered in. It looks to me like the System is getting more pervasive each year—more computerized and more methodical. There seem to be fewer "cracks" for us freedom lovers to slip between as time goes by. (Unless the System collapses, of course—but that's a whole other article.)

PROFESSIONAL PAPERCRETE

Universities and industrialists have been working with papercrete for years. (This is the meaning of the "busy airport" in the Little Fable at the beginning of this article.) They even have a biennial papercrete conference. Laura and I had the opportunity to meet with an industrial designer who showed us a video of a machine he had invented for producing papercrete roof shingles. The machine can make shingles that look like either slate, wood, or tile, and it really cranks out the production. Being accustomed to simple grassroots equipment like papercrete mixers, seeing the video of this sophisticated piece of equipment left us agog.

[I don't feel it is appropriate to use the industrial designer's name, since it was unclear to us if he really wanted to be associated with the grassroots papercrete movement.]

The formula he used was rather heavy on the cement—by weight, his formula was 90% cement and 10% paper—but there was no doubt that what he was working with was, indeed, papercrete.

We showed him one of Sean Sands' "bunker blocks" and he was not impressed. It needed far more cement, in his estimation, and had too much "give" to it.

He said that his research shows that unsealed papercrete can withstand about 50 wet/dry cycles before it starts to break down. So it is possible that people who are promoting "breathable" unsealed papercrete exposed to the weather will ultimately be in for a surprise.

He gave us the name of a university professor who is a key contact in the academic papercrete world: Prof. Ali A. Moslemi, with the Forest Products Dept. of the University of Idaho. Dr. Moslemi is evidently very busy, and we were never able to get ahold of him. For EQ readers who wish to investigate the technical aspects of papercrete, here is some contact information for Prof. Moslemi:

Phone: 208-885-6127
E-mail: amoslemi@novell.uidaho.edu
Web site: www.uidaho.edu/cfwr/forprod/amoslemi.html

SEAN'S DOMES REVISITED

This past summer Sean Sands' domes (which we described in issue 1, page 12) collapsed. Some pictures of his collapsed domes appeared on the Internet, and this created somewhat of a splash for awhile. (Nothing creates a splash for long on the Internet.) I was curious to hear what Sean had to say after he returned from his summer home in Canada and had a chance to inspect the damage. His assessment of the situation, which agrees with mine, is as follows: The main problem is that the domes were unsealed from

the rain. Heavy summer rains saturated the blocks with water, making them very heavy. When the domes were built, wet papercrete mortar was applied to dry papercrete blocks. The mortar shrank as it dried, causing it to pull away from the blocks, reducing structural integrity. The weak mortar joints were not able to withstand the weight of all that rainwater, and the domes collapsed. He is now moving away from using cement at all, and is now using paper adobe mortar (a mixture of paper and dirt) which adheres well to the blocks and shrinks less than papercrete mortar.

Using paper adobe mortar, Sean has rebuilt the dome that had the thickest walls, and has covered it with a sheet of 6-mil polyethylene ($10) for an absolute water seal. He then covered the plastic with a 2" layer of paper adobe to prevent UV damage to the plastic. He intends to paint the outer layer of paper adobe with waterproofing sealer, so that the dome will have two layers of protection from the rain.

This winter, Sean is experimenting with paper adobe, which will bring his building projects to a new level of sustainability and remarkably low cost (an estimated 14¢ per square foot for materials). We will be reporting on his latest projects in our next issue. Additionally, we will be running an article by Sean about the cordwood dome he built in British Columbia this past summer. Sean's construction research is focusing on three areas: (1) **sustainability**—using locally-available building materials whenever possible, (2) **ease and speed of construction**—get the outer shell completed as quickly as possible, and then finish the structure at your leisure, and (3) **low cost**—spending as little money as possible on materials. **Earth Quarterly** readers know of Sean only from his New Mexico projects that we described in our first issue, but he has constructed a number of low-cost structures in British Columbia, which we will be reporting on in future issues. Sean is taking shelter-building to the absolute limit in terms of quickness and low cost, and we are pleased to have the opportunity to describe his research in this magazine.

FLAME TESTS

Last issue, in our article, "Up in Smoke" on page 20, we reported on a couple of impromptu flame tests: Paul Salas found that a papercrete block, ignited by a piece of welding slag, smoldered overnight, and was completely reduced to 1/2 cup of ash residue. I reported that I was unable to get a Sean Sands "bunker block" to burn. Since then, we have several new reports:

Robert Secrest applied a propane torch to one spot on a papercrete block for 60 seconds. His experience was similar to Paul Salas'—the block burned very slowly, giving off tremendous heat but no smoke. He feels that such a fire would give off a great amount of carbon monoxide. He recommends experimenting with boric acid as a flame retardant.

At Mike McCain's fibrous cement workshop at WindTree Ranch on Oct. 10, participants ignited a papercrete block with a propane torch, with the usual results—an inconspicuous, yet very hot, slow-spreading fire. Don McKenzie of WindTree Ranch reported a flame experiment he performed—he set part of a low papercrete wall on fire and got the usual slow smolder. He put the fire out—or so he thought—and was surprised the next morning to find that the entire wall had been reduced to ash!

On Dec. 11 I duplicated Robert Secrest's flame test on three different papercrete blocks, a paper adobe block, and a piece of 2x6 lumber. In each case I applied the flame from a propane torch to one spot for one minute. The first block, which Mike McCain produced in Crestone, CO this past summer, did not burn. Neither did a Sean Sands "bunker block." The third block, which I produced, did the typical "slow burn." The paper adobe block did not burn. The piece of 2x6 burned with a large orange flame as long as the propane torch was applied, but went out as soon as the torch was removed.

I suspect that the Mike McCain block didn't burn because he is adding more cement than he used to. It's hard to get exact formula weights for papercrete, because people tend to measure by volume, not by weight. I do know that he is adding a full 94-pound bag of cement to a 200-gallon batch of slurry these days.

Sean Sands' block didn't burn, even though it contained a relatively small amount of cement, because he triple drained his slurry, resulting in a denser, less porous block, containing less air. Less air means less flammability.

Even though my block contained 50% more cement than Sean's, the slurry was only drained once, and the block was very porous, with plenty of air spaces to conduct oxygen to the fire.

The paper adobe block was manufactured by Bill Knauss of Tucson. By volume, the block is 70% paper, 25% clay, and 5% straw. By weight, it is about 2/3 clay and 1/3 paper. The straw contributes very little to the weight. The block didn't burn, probably because of both its high clay content and high density.

There seem to be two factors at work here—cement (or clay) content and density—that affect papercrete flammability. The higher the percentage of inflammable material, or the denser the block, the less likely it is to burn.

Papercrete burns in an insidiously slow way, and papercrete flammability needs to be thoroughly investigated. The next level of experimentation would be to build a papercrete wall, stucco it inside and out with different substances, and see how it burns, if at all.

STUCCO

There has been some concern about papercrete stucco not adhering adequately to a papercrete wall. I have had mixed results with by own project—even though I wet the wall before I applied experimental patches of papercrete stucco to it, sometimes the stucco stuck, and sometimes it didn't. (I'm talking about a couple of months after application here. All the patches of stucco stuck when I first put it on. After drying, some patches pulled right off, but others still seem to be firmly attached.) Mike McCain's latest technique is to make a mix of 40% "Stucco King" stucco mix, and 60% papercrete. This creates a hard (and probably inflammable) coating that bonds very tightly to papercrete. This is definitely worth a look by other experimenters.

WATERPROOFING

EQ subscriber Robert M. Carnes is searching for the ideal waterproofing agent for papercrete. He plans to move to Missouri, which has a wet climate. He writes:

"I have been looking for a sealer for the exterior of papercrete facilities.

"Mr. Bob Kreen of Blairstown Distributors, 2 Smith Road, Columbia, NJ 07832 has agreed to help us find a waterproofing agent.

"He desires some ice cube size blocks to start experimenting with. He is a rep for many companies in sealers, water repellents and waterproofers.

"Would you ask the people in the papercrete industry (one or two) to send Mr. Kreen about 20 ice cube blocks of papercrete.

"Please ask them to reference my name, Bob Carnes, and my call to him on 20 Nov. 98 so he will know what the cubes are for. I would appreciate it if whoever sends cubes lets me know so I can stay in the loop.

"I have also contacted several aviation paint companies that have new exotic water base paints. I'll keep trying to help us."

You can contact Bob Carnes at 1825 Lantern Drive, Asheboro, NC 27203-9780.

SQUISHING BLOCKS

Mike McCain had some observations about Travis Coffey's paper block factory that we wrote about last issue. Mike says that compressing wet slurry is not the way to go about it—you spend far too much time squeezing the water out of each block, and you end up with a block that is too dense, too heavy, doesn't contain enough air, and therefore is not as effective an insulator as it should be. A better way, Mike suggests, is to allow blocks to drain overnight, so that the water in between the paper fibers can be replaced by air. Then, the next day, when the blocks are still soft, a machine (which Mike hasn't built yet) can be used to gently and quickly squeeze the blocks to the proper shape and size (square corners, and a uniform size so that the blocks can be glued together rather than mortared together with slurry).

CONCLUSION

There's always the feeling that I've left something out, which is why there's always a next issue. In the meantime, I'd like to invite all you papercrete experimenters to share your successes, failures, ideas, photographs, and suggestions with the rest of us. That's what **Earth Quarterly** is here for.

Quotations from Chairman Mike

We have threatened to put out a "Little Red Book" of "Mikeisms," in the spirit of Chairman Mao's Little Red Book that was popular during the 60s. Here are some samples:

"Is fibrous cement labor intensive? It depends if it's your labor or mine."

"I know better; I don't always do better."

"If you're not failing, you're not trying hard enough."

"If you want to get impressed with numbers, that's really good—but the truth is, it really doesn't matter."

"Just because you can do something doesn't mean you should."

A Colorado Papercrete Tour

Gordon Solberg

Last September, Laura, Neil and I visited Crestone, Colorado, a charming little town nestled 8000 feet high in the foothills of the Sangre de Cristo Mountains of southern Colorado. We were the guests of Kelly and Rosana Hart, who took us to various papercrete construction sites in the Crestone area. Later, Mike McCain took us to a couple of his projects near Alamosa. Here's a report on what we found:

Kelly and Rosana built this little guest cottage first, to gain experience before tackling their house. This building, like their house, is a hybrid structure—earthbags covered with papercrete.

Earthbag construction, as described in EQ #2, pages 24-27, and EQ #3, pages 18-19, consists of woven polypropylene grain bags, filled with dirt or sand, and stacked on top of each other with barbed wire between the layers to keep the bags from slipping. This technique was pioneered by the Iranian architect Nader Khalili, and more information about it can be found on his web site: www.calearth.org.

One interesting feature of Kelly and Rosana's construction technique is that their bags are filled, not with dirt or sand, but with scoria. They don't know of anybody else who is doing this. Scoria is used as a decorative stone, and, like pumice, it has a lot of air pockets. But unlike pumice, which has closed air cells and will float on water, scoria has open air pockets, and will sink. But for insulation purposes, an air pocket is an air pocket, and scoria is a splendid insulator. They estimate that a finished scoria bag wall,

covered with papercrete, will have an R value of 40. As an added bonus, scoria provides considerable thermal mass as well as insulating value.

Here's another view of their guest cottage. The top of the building, which is lighter in color, has received only one stucco coat of papercrete. This base coat contains only paper and cement, is light in color, and has a lot of cracks in it, because papercrete without sand tends to crack as it dries.

The bottom layer is darker, because it contains sand. Sand helps prevent cracking when papercrete dries, and there is no visible cracking in the finish stucco coat.

Round window openings were made with culvert couplers. Kelly put rectangular pieces of glass over the round openings, and will cover the corners of the glass with papercrete.

The guest cottage has a diameter of 14 feet, which works out to 154 square feet. Including the window glass and a $200 wood stove, it cost about $1000. There is no plumbing or electricity.

This closeup shows the two stucco layers on the guest cottage. At the top of the photo is the base layer, with cracks. If you look closely, you can see 2" chickenwire which will help hold the finish coat. At the bottom of the photo is the finish coat, with distinctive

finger marks caused by patting the papercrete into place. Ultimately, the stucco will be lightly stained to a golden color.

This is the bedroom part of their house, which, at the time this picture was taken, had only the base coat of papercrete

stucco—hence the cracks.

Their house is two earthbag domes with a connecting passageway. The floor area is over 1000 square feet. Including lofts, total useable space is over 1200 square feet. Total cost, including appliances, windows and doors, is around $10,000— about $10 a square foot.

Their soil is essentially sand, so lack of drainage is not a problem. The foundation is a trench filled with scoria. There is nothing that will be harmed by water. The polypropylene bags will not rot, and are vulnerable only to solar ultraviolet radiation. The scoria inside the bags will not wick water. Kelly and Rosana intend to leave the outside of their house unsealed, so that the walls will be able to breathe.

Speaking of foundations, Nader Khalili recommends that earthbag houses not be locked to the earth. You don't want to pin them onto a solid concrete slab. Instead, you allow the earth to move in relation to the house, and by doing so you eliminate a lot of the stresses that houses go through in an earthquake. If you let a house roll with the punches, it's not as likely to be torn apart. Khalili has done a great amount of engineering work on the earthbag concept, including earthquake tests, so the groundwork for codes acceptance has already been done.

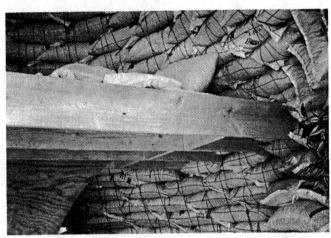

The framework for the sleeping loft is an integral part of the wall, which strengthens both the wall and the loft.

Saguache County, Colorado, where Crestone is located, has no building codes for the structural aspect of the building. The county has not adopted the uniform building code, although buildings are subject to the state electrical and plumbing inspections and codes. In the Baca Grande subdivision, where most of the houses in this article are located, there is a committee that oversees the design of a house in terms of appearance, but they don't pass judgment on the structural aspects. The Wild West still exists!

Here's a view of the unfinished interior of their bedroom. For window frames, they are using culvert couplers and wagon wheels. They bought 4000 polypropylene bags, in bales of 1000, from Cady Bag Co. (see Cady's ad in this issue).

Most of the bags are folded over at the ends, but some of the bags were stitched closed. This allows the bag to be longer without their contents spilling out. He used stitched bags to build the pillars and arches.

59

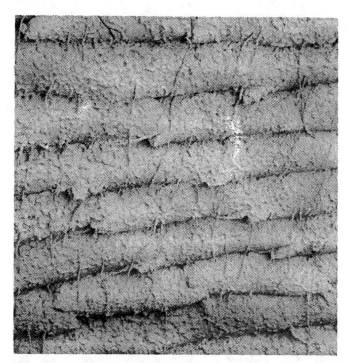

fast way to stucco a building. He thinks a finished job would require three coats of stucco. The stucco would be anywhere from 2-7" thick, depending on whether you're talking about the surface of the bags, or the cracks in between bags.

The scoria they used was mined just south of Alamosa. It costs $20 a ton. They bought an 18-ton truckload—25 yards—which cost them $700 delivered. Shipping just about doubled the cost.

Scoria is useful, not just for walls and foundation trenches, but for putting down an insulating subfloor. Just lay down a pad of scoria, 6-8 inches thick, and cover this with adobe, tile, brick, or flagstone. The scoria will insulate those thermal mass materials from the earth.

Not all the bags were filled with scoria. Some of them are filled with sand from the site. Sandbags are useful for providing a high thermal mass, and Kelly and Rosana used them in applications where the bags could be stacked vertically, such as platforms and pillars. But this is very fine sand, and sand is a shape-shifter, so Kelly and Rosana wouldn't feel comfortable if their entire house had been built with sandbags. Bags filled with scoria hold their shape much better, and are more appropriate for the high, inward-curving walls of their house.

In addition to the two strands of 4-point barbed wire between each row to keep the bags from slipping, the bags are tied together vertically with baling twine. This not only provides extra strength, but will give the inside stucco a little extra to grab onto.

Here's an experiment that worked. Kelly mixed up some stucco, which he calls a "weak cement stucco," consisting of 8 parts sand, one part cement, and one part lime. Then he mixed this 50/50 with papercrete. He used a diaphragm pump that is used in mines, which is capable of pumping gravel. The pump was so powerful, he had to hold the nozzle like a water cannon. The slurry load was pumped so quickly that he didn't have much control. But the stucco stuck to the bags without having to use wire mesh, and it got blown at high pressure into every crevice. This would be a very

Here Kelly demonstrates the miracle of the arch, by standing on a single row of scoria bags placed into an arch configuration.

You would think that the whole thing would just collapse, leaving Kelly and the scoria bags laying in a heap on the ground, but instead the downward pressure is transferred laterally along the arch and thence down to the ground. It must have been a major "Aha!" experience to whoever first discovered the arch concept thousands of years ago.

Hartley Spencer of Crestone was building a hybrid monolithic dome at the time we visited. Since then, health problems have prevented him from completing his dome. But his project was an intriguing one, and we want to mention it here. This photo shows the curved rebar framework for his 900-square-foot dome. He was using what is called an "eco shell," an inflatable inner liner which can be used repeatedly. He planned to inflate the eco-shell with air, and then shoot a 3" layer of shotcrete to form the skin for his dome. After the concrete was hard, he would have waterproofed it. Then—and now it starts getting really interesting—he planned to put a layer of straw bales on the outside of the dome. This is why all the window openings are shaped like turrets, sticking out two feet from the rebar framework. Then, using his shotcrete pump, he planned to cover the straw bales with a layer of papercrete. Thus, his house would have had lots of thermal mass, covered with a thick layer of insulation that would have had an R value of at least 40.

Last issue we printed some photos of Mike's tow mixer, and his moveable forms utilizing motorcycle wheels. This issue, we

have some pictures of Mike's Colorado projects, and some examples of the impressive production capabilities he developed. In this photo, Mike shows a large papercrete block he made.

Some people persist in believing that papercrete still isn't "for real," that people are just sort of fooling around, experimenting with it in their backyards. I hope this picture conveys something of the enormous production capability Mike developed in Crestone during the summer of 1998.

Down the center of the picture is a row, at least 100 feet long, of roof panels made with a drag form. Along the right side of the picture are batches of blocks made with the moveable form pictured in our last issue, page 14. It is possible, with a tow mixer, some simple forms, and a small crew of dedicated workers, to produce a considerable tonnage of papercrete blocks in a day.

Incidentally, when describing Mike's tow mixer last issue, I said that we hadn't transcribed the tapes yet, and didn't know exactly how much sand he added to a mixer load. Having transcribed the tapes, I can now report than a mixer load contains 4 5-gallon buckets of sand, as well as a full 94-pound bag of cement and a heaping wheelbarrow load of magazines (but not EQ, at least not that we know of).

In the past, Mike used only 1/2 bag of cement per load, but he likes the results when he uses a full bag—the blocks harden up a lot faster, and are considerably stronger. Sand is a very important contribution to the mix. Without sand, or without sufficient cement, you get a lot more cracking when the papercrete dries.

These are "jumbo blocks." One tow mixer batch will make 4 jumbo blocks. Each block is a nominal 30" long, 16" wide, and 16" deep. However, because of settling and shrinkage, the blocks are

This is Ocean and Dylan's house, with the walls and roof up, but not yet stuccoed. The sloppier the blocks are put up, the more nooks and crannies there will be for the stucco to adhere to. The main room is a 22-foot circle, which works out to 380 square feet. It cost them $1000 for materials, which Mike says is way overpriced—they spent a lot more than they needed to before he showed up on the scene.

actually 15" wide and 14" deep. Six jumbo blocks stacked on top of each other make a wall that's 8 feet high. They are designed to be easily lifted by two people when dry.

Mike puts a sandbag in the bottom of the form to make a clean block—otherwise, the papercrete will adhere to whatever sticks and stones are lying on the ground. He pours in the slurry, and the form can be lifted off in 20 minutes. Thus, you don't need a lot of forms to make a lot of blocks. It takes these blocks about a month to totally dry out, but they can be put in a wall within 2 days if necessary, though they are very heavy when they are still this wet.

Each form has a vertical 2x4 at each end, creating a 2x4" groove at the end of each block. When two blocks are put end to end, there is a 4" square hole between the blocks. Mike fills this hole with papercrete mortar and squeezes it down with his fist. This not only squeezes mortar between the blocks, but forms a dense, 4x4" mortar "plug" that, being stronger than the adjacent blocks, serves to key the blocks together.

Jumbo blocks are more trouble to make, because the forms are so high the mixer can't be driven over them. So mortar has to be shoveled into the forms. Their advantage is that a wall can be built from them very quickly.

Papercrete blocks shrink as they dry, resulting in a tapered block—the top is narrower than the bottom. Mike says this taper is a good thing. You can put two tapers together to give your wall an interesting look. Or, with the tapers down, you create a shelf for the stucco to hold onto.

Mike uses a 60/40 stucco blend—60% papercrete, 40% stucco mix, as developed by Eric Patterson. (See our article about Eric Patterson in EQ #2.) This blend goes on in one coat, adheres very well to papercrete, dries hard, and never cracks. For stuccoing the inside wall, Mike recommends a blend of 60% papercrete and 40% plaster.

Here's an interesting hybrid—an exterior privacy/windbreak wall made of straw bales, and covered with papercrete. In this photo, Mike demonstrates his stuccoing technique. He recommends using a small trowel so you get a lot of pressure. He started by throwing the papercrete at the straw bale wall to get it to stick. No chickenwire was used. Once the first papercrete coat is on, it's easy to add more coats. The straw bales were stacked up in a sloppy way, and the papercrete stucco "can easily cover up a lot of sin," as Mike puts it. Papercrete can be troweled on up to 2" thick in a single application to smooth out variations in wall thickness. Since papercrete is so lightweight, no stress is put on the wall. If cement stucco was applied this thickly without chickenwire, it would break loose under its own weight and fall off.

While we're on the subject of straw bales, Mike has an idea for a hybrid straw bale/papercrete block. You build a form, put a straw bale in the form, and then cast papercrete around the bale to give a uniform structural block. Since most of the volume is straw, less papercrete mixing is required. Such a block could be pre-finished before you put it in the wall, and there would be no need for chickenwire.

This is Abi's partially-completed house in Crestone. The jumbo block walls give the house an Inca look. This house, even before it is completed, looks like a ruin. Since all human structures will eventually become ruins, papercrete construction offers us a quick preview of the ultimate fate of our human endeavors.

A 2002 PAPERCRETE HOUSE

This is a 1400 square foot papercrete addition built by Mike Osbourne in Mimbres, NM. This photo was taken in March 2002.

Mike says, "This addition came about when we were given a bunch of doors and windows that were being replaced. Papercrete seemed to be the (continued on p. 65)

Here's another view of Abi's house, showing the towering 14,000-foot Sangre de Cristo mountains in the background. To build what you see here took 9 half-days of actual working time by two men. (This does not include the time spent making the blocks.) They used jumbo blocks only on the bottom courses, because the blocks were still wet, and heavy to lift. Mike cut the window openings with a chainsaw. This house will ultimately have a papercrete floor.

This is Christine's house, still not completed, which was built in 2½ weeks of actual working time in October 1997. Built on a rubble trench footer, the house is 700 square feet, and used $900 worth of cement. Since winter was coming on, Mike was in a hurry to get this house finished. The last step was the roof. Mike put 1" chickenwire over the rafters and put on a layer of slurry. After the slurry dried, he used a diaphragm pump and pumped 6 tons of papercrete onto the roof.

63

It snowed the next day. Worse, the house was left unheated for two weeks after completion, and the roof froze solid as an iceberg. Even though the occupants built large fires in their wood heater to try to dry out the roof, it stayed wet until spring, and grew a lush coating of mold on the inside. The roof finally dried out during the summer, Mike scraped off the mold, and the roof seems none the worse for wear. Mike doesn't advise building this way, however—it's much better to build with papercrete during the warmer months of the year, so that new construction has plenty of time to dry out before winter.

This house has a tar roof. Mike says that $35 worth of hot tar can cover a 1000-square-foot roof. The hot tar soaks into the papercrete, and will not come loose or crack. He plans to put on a second coat of tar, and cover this with sand for a more esthetically pleasing appearance.

This photo shows the roof rafter design for Christine's house. The rebar, which was installed for additional bracing, proved unnecessary.

The next day, Mike showed us the first two papercrete structures he ever built. This one is a wool processing facility north of Alamosa, CO. It started out as a prefab garage, and then the owners had Mike build a papercrete wing on each side. This is the structure that Mike built to code (see EQ #1, page 13). The code specified a footer dug 2 feet into the ground. However, this area has a seasonally high water table—sometimes the water is only 1½ feet down. It would have made more sense not to have gone down into the water, but codes are codes. It would have taken $2000 to

pour a concrete footer 16" wide, so they did it with papercrete for $300. Remember that a papercrete wall weighs only one pound per square inch, so a massive foundation isn't necessary. However, papercrete wicks water, so the footer for this structure wicks water up into the wall whenever the water table is high. There is no structural settling or cracking of the wall, though a surface crack in the stucco, caused by not using sand in the stucco, is visible here. If an adobe wall was built on a footer that wicked water like this, the adobe would turn to mush. After three years, the structure is standing up to the weather and wicking so far.

Here's an inside view of the wool house, showing fleeces drying on wooden racks. The floor in the garage part of the building is solid concrete; the floor in the papercrete part is a 2" slab of concrete poured over a papercrete subfloor. This combination concrete/papercrete floor was noticeably warmer than the solid concrete, and also absorbed the impact of our feet when we walked on it, much like a wooden floor.

Then we drove south of Alamosa to the Snail House, which is mentioned in EQ #1, page 14. The owner raises escargot snails in the middle part of this structure. Except for the rafters and door frames, this building is entirely made of papercrete. Mike didn't know how big the door was going to be when he built the structure, so he constructed a narrow door opening. Later, when he knew exactly how big the door was going to be, he took a chainsaw and made a nice straight cut through the papercrete to exactly the right dimensions. There are few other building materials you can do this with.

The roof is of considerable interest here—it is made of

unsealed papercrete, yet doesn't leak water. The roof panels are 2x4 feet, and were made using 2x4" forms on the ground. When the panels were dry, they were lifted onto the roof and screwed onto the rafters, then covered with a couple of additional inches of slurry. No rebar or wire mesh was used—just papercrete panels screwed to the rafters. Snails require a high-humidity environment, so when the building was first built, the owner decided to soak the roof to raise the humidity inside the building. He threw a garden hose onto the roof and let it run for six hours. This is an incredible amount of water, and a lot of weight. Mike was concerned that the rafters might crack, or that the papercrete panels would collapse. But the roof, totally saturated, held up. Water started to wick down the walls, but surprisingly, water didn't drip from the ceiling as you might expect.

This is far more water than the weather would ever bring at any one time, and indicates how well papercrete holds water. Any rainwater or snowmelt is absorbed by the roof, and the winds quickly evaporate the moisture from the surface. Even if the roof was completely saturated with water, it wouldn't leak—as the impromptu garden hose experiment revealed. The owner, by the way, decided that he couldn't get a high enough humidity by soaking the roof, so he now soaks the papercrete floor instead.

The right side of the building is used for housing chickens. You might think that chickens would peck at papercrete, and they will before it has dried. But papercrete becomes very hard once it cures out, and chickens leave it alone.

Here's a view of the back of the chicken house, showing the tilt-up panel design. Mike recommends this method above all others, if you have a way to tilt the panels into position. Each panel was poured flat on the ground, with two vertical pieces of rebar and three horizontal pieces embedded in it. Each piece of rebar stuck out from the panel a few inches. The owner of the building used a front-end loader to tilt the panels vertically. Then, using a sledgehammer, he drove the vertical rebar down into the papercrete foundation, and the horizontal rebar into the adjacent panels. So the entire structure is pinned together with rebar. A concrete foundation can be used, if holes are predrilled to accept the rebar. At the corners, he pinned the panels with rebar driven in at a 45° angle, so it won't pull apart.

The roof is hard to see in this picture, but if you look right above the rafters, you will get an idea of how thick the papercrete panels are. The roof has a modest slope, but there is no runoff from it—all moisture is absorbed by the papercrete, and evaporates back into the air when the weather dries out. This roof has held up without leaking for 3 years now. As reported in EQ #3, page 16, an industrial designer told us that his experiments indicate that papercrete starts to break down after about 50 wet/dry cycles. It

will be interesting to monitor this building as the years go by, and see how well the roof holds up.

Here's a view inside the snail house, showing how the snails are raised in boxes raised off the ground. Our publisher, on the right side of the picture, holds her ever-present tape recorder, so that not a single factoid can escape. The temperature is kept at 85°, at a humidity of 90%, and the papercrete floor is kept constantly soaked. Even under these rainforest conditions, the papercrete is holding up well after 3 years.

Our Colorado papercrete tour offers several examples of how papercrete is being used in the real world. Most of these structures have a rough-and-ready appearance, and not a single one of them is totally finished. But hopefully, experimenters will be inspired by them to try their own papercrete structures.

What the papercrete movement needs now are some built-from-scratch papercrete houses that express a more middle-class ideal—high ceilings, square corners, and large windows. Personally, I love "Hobbit holes" and houses that look like toadstools or ant hills, but people always ask us, here at EQ HQ, "Are there any papercrete houses that look like normal houses?" The answer is, "Yes, Eric Patterson's house, pictured in EQ #2, is as normal as can be. It could pass for 'Santa Fe adobe.'" But it's an addition to his adobe house, not a 100%, built-from-the-ground-up papercrete house. When we start seeing total papercrete houses that middle-class America can relate to, that's when you'll start hearing about papercrete everywhere.

2002 PAPERCRETE HOUSE (cont. from p. 63) cheapest way to build walls around them. I used a regular sand/cement mortar to put the blocks together because of the speed at which it sets up. Also, I actually got a building permit from the state. They were very helpful about filling out the forms and were quite enthusiastic about the process. My addition was permitted under the adobe construction regulations, so there is some overkill on the insulation requirements. Better overkill than underkill."

Mike's email address is:

<mikeos44@hotmail.com>.

An Innovative Papercrete Dome Design

James Moon

Editor's Note: Last issue we briefly described a papercrete dome built in 1983-84 by James Moon of Tucson, AZ, utilizing an innovative framework of interlocking rings of electrical conduit. In the mid-80s, James started a company, "Harmony Domes," to promote this dome concept. The following article consists of an informational brochure and a short article that he wrote at that time. Since then, he has moved on to new projects, and is no longer interested in talking about his domes. As we mentioned last issue, he requested that we not use his real name, nor print his address. We'd like to thank James for allowing us to print this information, and we hope that it inspires experimenters out there to try some of these ideas. All photos are by James Moon.

The Brochure

Here is a revolutionary construction process by which a fire resistant, termite proof, superinsulated shell can be built for three dollars a square foot.

14 ft. diameter, 9 ft. high dome

The frame is covered with wire mesh. We used 1" by 2" 14-gauge welded wire screen. 3 or 4 layers of chicken wire would work. This in turn is covered with a mixture of newspaper and cement, 1 lb. of dry paper to 1 lb. of cement. This mixture has an insulation value of about R-4 per inch. Starting at the bottom, build a wall about 6" high, and the desired thickness. Continue around and up, like an igloo.

20 ft. diameter, 4 ft. high "trussless roof"

The framework is composed of a series of 3/4 inch conduit steel rings. Rings are formed by drawing a circle on the ground, and bending the pipe at 2 ft. increments with a conduit bender to match the circle. Ring sections are connected with sleeve connectors, arranged in a circular pattern, indented and bolted at intersections with 1/4 inch carriage bolts. U-bolts make assembly easier and stronger, if available.

The interior and exterior is finished with a mixture of paper and plaster. We used 1 part wet paper pulp to 1 1/2 parts plaster. Add more water if necessary.

66

The completed structure is then covered with a waterproof material which can be tinted to any desired shade. We used a fabric base coated with 3 coats of vinyl acrylic roof paint. In humid climates, paint interior with roof paint for vapor barrier.

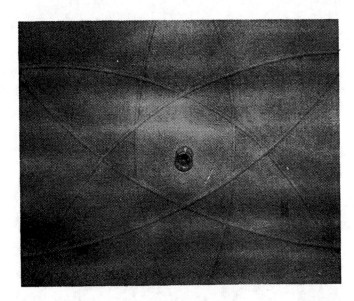

The exposed interior framework creates an attractive geometrical pattern.

The Article

This article briefly describes a new type of structure based on a framework using large rings of thinwall steel tubing, arranged in a geometrical pattern.

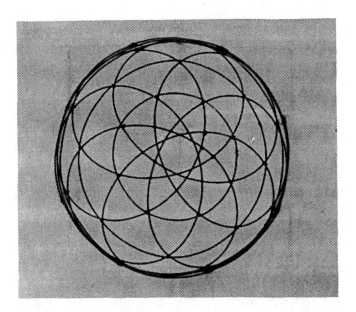

**Scale model of 24 ft. diameter, 12 ft. high dome
8 main rings 18 ft. diameter**
Building a scale model out of wire is very useful.

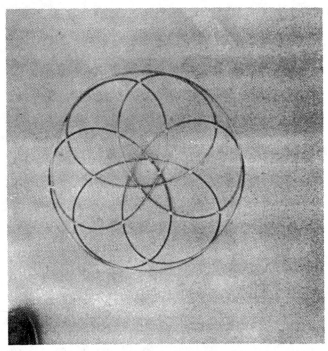

**SCALE MODEL OF FRAMEWORK
Top View**

SCALE MODEL
Side View

COMPLETED FRAME

The remaining sections of each ring are joined to form the walls and the base of the frame. The roof section is then attached, completing the entire frame.

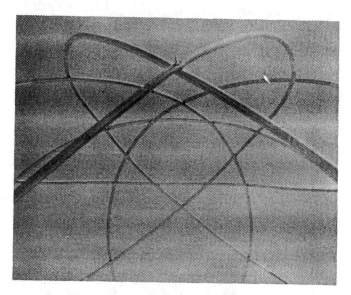

POETRY IN STEEL

Because the basic components are circular, there are no joints, only intersecting arcs. This results in a frame that is extremely rugged, economical, and lightweight.

ROOF SECTION

Each ring is divided into three sections, and one section of each ring is used to assemble the entire roof structure. This assembly can be done on the ground, greatly simplifying construction.

DOORS AND WINDOWS ADDED

The large opening at the lower half of the frame provides ample space for the addition of doors and windows.

INTERIOR VIEW

The entire structure is covered with welded wire screen. This greatly increases the structural strength and provides a base for the insulation layer.

READY TO COVER

At this stage the framework is ready for electrical wiring, which is simply tied to the outside of the screen.

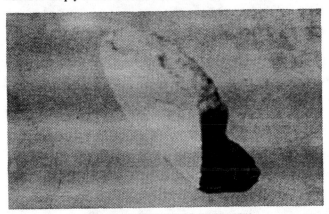

"YESTERDAY'S NEWS"

The insulation layer is composed of old newspaper combined with water and cement in a cement mixer. The resulting composition is fireproof, termite proof, has a high insulation value, and it's practically free.

"TODAY'S BUILDING MATERIALS"

Four pounds of newspaper combined with six pounds of cement makes one cubic foot of material. A 4-inch-thick layer of paper costs about 20 cents a square foot.

69

INTERIOR PARTLY FINISHED

The interior is finished with a mixture of plaster and paper, and the exterior is weatherproofed with a mixture of waterproof cement and vermiculite.

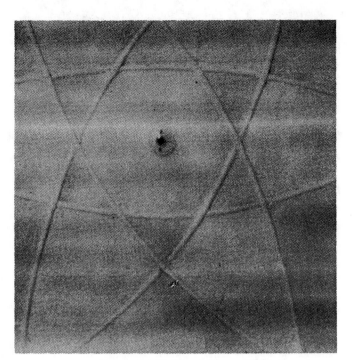

COMPLETED INTERIOR

Different colors can be used to accent the geometry.

COMPLETED PAPER SHELL

The total cost of materials for a 20 foot diameter, 10 foot high dome is about $700.

COMPLETED EXTERIOR

Painted white, the exterior reflects the desert sun.

Projects

Here are a couple of projects that EQ readers might be interested in:

1. Bill Knauss, a rammed earth builder from Tucson, wants to set up a land trust, alternative economic system, and paper block factory somewhere in the Southwest. If you are interested, call him at 602-623-9706.

2. An eco-village is forming on 200 acres of land in the Ozarks of NW Arkansas. Lifetime land stewardship titles are available from $800 to $7000, for parcels ranging in size from 2100 square feet to 3.3 acres. For more information, call 1-800-503-5606, or e-mail Jessica Crandall at <jessicacrandall@usa.net>.

An Electric Barrel Mixer for Papercrete

Kelly Hart

During the summer of 1997 I made an electric barrel mixer for making papercrete, based on some of the designs that Mike McCain showed me. In fact he provided me with the barrel and the motor. Since I planned to use the machine with my photovoltaic system and inverter, I needed to use a fairly small motor, and the 1/3 hp motor that had been used for commercial food mixing seemed like it might be ideal. It had a 1/2" shaft with a coupler already attached that could be used to connect it to my mixing spindle.

This photo shows the 55 gallon, heavy duty plastic drum that serves as the tank for the mixer. A half-moon hole was cut out of the top, removing only about 1/3 of the plastic. This left enough of the original plastic top to mount the motor directly to the plastic, with the shaft sticking through a hole (slightly offset from the exact center of the barrel, in order to have enough room to mount the motor). I was able to mount the motor securely to the top of the barrel with 4 bolts going up through the plastic and into female threads on the motor housing. The other hole I had to cut in the barrel was at the base for a drain plug. I mounted a 3" PVC fitting with threads to accept a 3" threaded plug. This fitting was firmly attached to the barrel by tightening a similar threaded fitting on the inside of the barrel to the external one. This drain leaks a little water when in use, but not enough to be a problem.

This photo shows a view through the top of the barrel, where you can see two major features. On the right is a 2x6" wooden baffle, about 3 feet long, that is mounted to the inside of the barrel. The 6" dimension points toward the center, and the board is secured to the barrel with several lag bolts screwed in from the outside of the barrel. This baffle forces the paper slurry into the spinning blades and sets up a churning action.

The other element visible in this photo is the spindle and blade arrangement. This is composed of a section of 1/2" threaded rod long enough to reach from the motor coupling to near the bottom of the barrel. The two blades are 4" squares of stainless steel sheet metal, with a 1/2" hole drilled in the center of each, and then tightened onto the shaft with 1/2" washers and nuts on either side of each blade. They are about one foot apart, and situated about in the middle of the barrel. The tips of the square blades are alternately bent up and down. What cannot be seen in the photo is a stabilizer at the base of the mixer. This is made of a 3/4" galvanized pipe flange, with a 2" nipple screwed into it. The flange is bolted directly to the base of the mixer with bolts through the plastic, so that it is vertically directly below the motor shaft. So, when the threaded rod is inserted into the nipple, and then tightened onto the motor shaft with the coupling, the blade arrangement doesn't wobble much.

That's pretty much it as far as the mechanics of the mixer goes. Next, I'll describe how I use it. First I fill the mixer with enough water to cover at least the lower blade, and then I turn on the motor and start throwing in the newspaper, which has been soaking overnight in another barrel. I have found that newspaper turns into a slurry much easier than other kinds of tougher paper.

This photo shows how I tear sections of newspaper into roughly quarters, and toss them into the mixer. I'll keep the water flowing slowly into the mix until it reaches a level about 6 or 8 inches below the top of the barrel, and I'll add paper until the slurry starts to thicken and look sort of like cottage cheese, as shown in the next photo:

If you add too much paper, the churning action will stop, and you're kind of stuck, unless you drain some out and add more water. It usually takes 15 to 20 minutes to mix a batch.

Occasionally some of the newspaper will wrap around the spindle and slow down the action of the machine. If this happens, it is best to stop the motor, reach down with your hand, and tear the paper away from the spindle. With the square blades, the paper almost never gets bound up in the blades, as it did when I first experimented with a rectangular edger blade.

Once the slurry is the right consistency, I add two heaping shovel-fulls of Portland cement, and let the mixer run for another 5 minutes, or until the cement has thoroughly mixed with the paper,

which you can tell by the color. The churning action will mix it all pretty well, so you can just watch and see when no more paper without cement (lighter gray) comes up from below; then you can shut off the machine.

Since I'm using the papercrete as an outside coating over my sandbag buildings, I need to drain some of the water out of the slurry to make the stuff into a clay-like consistency. I do this by draining the slurry into a drain box,

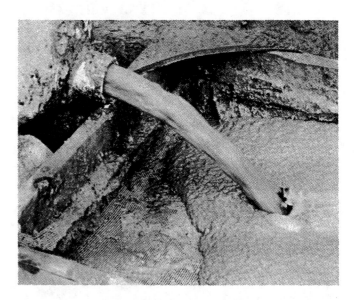

which is just a rectangular frame made from 2x8s or 2x10s, whatever is big enough to hold one full load from the barrel. Tacked to the bottom of the wooden frame is some screen or netting that will allow the water to drain through, but keep the paper pulp in. This box has about 1/8" fiberglass stucco lath on the bottom, but I have also used common window screen.

I'll let the water drain out (this could be captured and reused, if water conservation is desirable) for about a half hour, or until I can easily scoop the papercrete out:

I like to use the stuff when it will form softball sized balls that can easily be pushed into the crevices between the bags.

(Continued on page 74)

Slurry with Shorty

This past May we were making hundreds of blocks in preparation for our workshop. When you have your paper block factory on the shoulder of the highway (see photo below), all kinds of people stop by to see what you're doing.

It's a splendid magnet that draws papercreters, adobe block makers, and other "hands on" types. One day Shorty Inderdahl showed up at our work site. We got to talking, and it turns out that he is one of the original second generation papercreters. His reputation had preceded him—when I was having my mixer welded last summer (see EQ #2), the welder told me that there was a guy in Salem, NM who was building with papercrete. This guy, we learned later, was Shorty Inderdahl.

Shorty was intrigued by a newspaper article about Eric Patterson several years ago, so he drove over to Silver City to meet Eric and see what he was up to. Shorty liked what he saw, so he built himself a mixer and started making blocks.

Working in his spare time, Shorty has accumulated quite a pile of blocks over the years. Using steel forms that he made himself, he makes blocks that are approximately 10" wide, 24" long, and 7" deep. He uses Eric Patterson's formula—cement and paper, with no sand. On the right side of the picture are some of his papercrete logs. He was the first person to make logs, that we know of. He plans to use these blocks to wall off the ends of his steel Quonset hut.

Here's a closeup of his logs. The longest ones are 10 feet long. When he started out, he built a mixer based on Eric Patterson's design, with an "S" shaped blade. But he is no longer using this mixer. He has found it more convenient to get shredded computer paper from a local bank, and mix this with cement in a regular cement mixer.

Your editor hefts one of Shorty's logs single-handed.

After papercrete or paper adobe slurry is poured into a form, it shrinks as the excess water drains out. This results in a tapered block, narrower at the top than the bottom, with sloping sides. This isn't really a problem, but you have to apply a thicker coat of mortar when mortaring the blocks together or applying the stucco coat, to compensate for the irregularities of the blocks.

Shorty has developed an easy way to eliminate this taper. He just lays a 1½" thick piece of wood on the top of the form after he has poured the slurry in. This isn't enough weight to compress the block and reduce the R value, but it greatly reduces the taper.

In this photo, Shorty demonstrates how his wooden block fits into the form. Notice the long pieces of wood at the ends. These prevent the wooden block from sinking more than 1½" into the form as the slurry settles. Not only that, but the slurry can't settle more than 1½", due to vacuum action. So the blocks are all a uniform thickness. After the slurry has set up for a day, he removes the lid and the form so that the block can start drying.

Blocks with square corners are ideal for people who want to glue or pin their blocks together. And these blocks can be mortared together with very little mortar. Shorty has experimented with gluing blocks together with the urethane foam insulation you buy in a spray can. This makes a very strong bond.

Shorty is working on a number of experiments, and we will let you know how they turn out. You can call him at 505-267-1538.

TIGHT FIT DEPT.

Greg Jay tries on a tow mixer for size. This is not recommended when the mixer is being towed.

Electric Barrel Mixer
(Continued from page 72)

I have used this machine to mix maybe 100 batches of papercrete, and it's still going strong. At some point I would expect the spindle shaft to wear out from friction with the pipe bearing at the bottom of the barrel, at which point I will need to either replace the section of treaded rod, or just install a slightly longer nipple on the stabilizer. I have only used the machine to make pure papercrete (newspaper and cement). I suspect that if I tried to add much sand or adobe, that the mixer couldn't handle it.

A Papercrete Workshop at WindTree Ranch

To the best of our knowledge, the papercrete workshop that was held at WindTree Ranch, near Douglas, AZ, in October 1998 was only the second such workshop that had ever been held. By the time that workshop rolled around, Laura and I felt like seasoned old pros—**Earth Quarterly** had been out for 5 months, we had interviewed all the major papercrete movers and shakers, we had mixed dozens of loads of slurry ourselves and were halfway through with our papercrete office, and in our outreach activities we had encountered, not only a lot of enthusiasm about papercrete, but an enormous amount of skepticism as well. Thousands of people had seen our "Paper block houses, 75¢ a square foot" classified ads and had given them a pass, because it was obviously a scam, right? It's <u>impossible</u> to build a house for 75¢ a square foot these days, right? So Laura and I were curious to see how a bunch of real, live people, who had never seen papercrete before, would respond to a papercrete workshop. Admittedly, this was a pre-selected group of open-minded people who were intrigued enough by papercrete to spend actual money on a workshop, but we were interested to see the learning process in action.

It was a fascinating process to watch. The first morning was spent listening to Mike McCain talk about papercrete, and people busily took notes and absorbed information. But it wasn't until after lunch, when Mike fired up the mixer and mixed the first batch of slurry, that the collective light bulb turned on: "You mean it's really that easy? You mean that's all there is to it? All you do is mix up a soup of this stuff, pour it into forms, and let it harden?" By the end of the second day, the participants were seasoned old pros themselves, and were enthusiastically planning their own papercrete projects. There's nothing like seeing something with your own eyes to make you a believer, which is why we've made a video to go along with this book.

Mike adds water to a tow mixer. This particular mixer was being used in "stationary mode"—one of the wheels had been removed, and a driveshaft connected the tow mixer to the rear wheel of a truck that was being used as the power source. This is exactly the same type of setup that was used by Sean Sands and Mike McCain at City of the Sun in the spring of 1998, that was described at length in EQ #1. This shows how versatile tow mixers are—they can either be towed behind a vehicle, or used in stationary mode.

This closeup shows the "valve" for the tow mixer—a toilet float inserted into a piece of 4"-diameter PVC pipe, held in place by a screwdriver. Quick, simple, and it works great.

Workshop participants dump slurry for a root cellar floor slab. Papercrete slurry looks just like concrete in photographs, but it is much lighter in weight and easier to move around.

This is known as getting into your work. Workshop participants trowel the papercrete floor slab.

Here's another one of Mike's ideas. Take two metal "tin can studs" and bolt them together, forming a rigid I-beam. You

use these I beams as roof rafters. Between the rafters, use papercrete slabs of the correct size to slip into the metal studs. He was using two ordinary blocks to illustrate the concept here— papercrete roof panels could be considerably longer and wider than this.

Here are a couple of papercrete forms developed by Mike. It's an improvement on the ages-old adobe form. The handle is so you don't have to bend over to move the form, and the lid is used to squish down the slurry to fill in the corners of the blocks.

This view of the form shows the hinged lid. Three shovelfuls of slurry are dumped into the form, the lid is closed, and then you stand on the lid, putting considerable pressure on it and ensuring an evenly-packed block.

This particular form has rounded sheetmetal corners. Mike designed it for a friend who wanted a more decorative block for a garden wall. He likes this design, because the rounded corners allow you to easily add mortar between the blocks.

Earth Quarterly Builds a Paper Office

This article was originally intended for EQ #2. We are finally printing it 11 months later.

For the past three years Laura and I have been putting out *Dry Country News*, and now **Earth Quarterly**, from a corner of our living room. This past summer seemed to be the time to reclaim our personal living space by giving our publishing business a home of its own, so we decided to build a little office next to our house. Papercrete seemed the obvious choice for the building material.

The spot we had in mind was a little area dug into the bank of the Rio Grande. We had space for one room 8x16 feet, and another room, at a lower level, 10x13 feet. Since our building site was rectangular, a building with square corners was the obvious choice. I decided to pour the slurry directly into forms, eliminating the blockmaking process entirely.

First, we had to collect some raw materials. Here, Laura displays a vanload of newspapers and rolls of

newsprint she obtained for free from our local daily paper, the Las Cruces *Sun-News*. There is a huge supply of paper out there, just waiting to be turned into papercrete. Potential sources include newspaper and magazine publishers, print shops (see the article on Eric Patterson in EQ #2), municipal recycling centers (which will sell bales of paper for a very reasonable price), and friends and neighbors.

You, too, can have a beautiful pile of waste paper in your backyard!

Like the test pilots in Tom Wolfe's book, *The Right Stuff*, who were always "pushing the envelope," I decided to test the outer edge of the papercrete envelope. You never find the limits of what's possible until you exceed them. When a test pilot pushes the envelope too far, he becomes a spew of confetti strewn across the desert floor. When a papercrete builder pushes the envelope too far, his plywood warps. But the principle is the same.

I decided to start with a very ambitious plywood form. Start big, and see what I could get away with—I could always scale it back later if necessary. My first form consisted of two sheets of 3/4" plywood, spaced 8" apart. Filling it with slurry would give me a large hunk of wall, 4 feet high and 8 feet long. Such a tall form is very unstable, so I had to brace it with 2x4s. The form was screwed together with steel corner braces. The plywood was painted with two coats of linseed oil.

I set the form on a strip of plastic directly on the ground, in a misguided attempt to dispense with a foundation. After talking to Eric Patterson, and learning how much trouble he has had with water seeping into the bottom of his papercrete dome, I decided to build a modest

concrete foundation for the rest of the building. More foundation details appear later in this article.

I started by filling the form only half full. I knew that a form this high full of wet slurry would be a potential disaster waiting to happen, so I proceeded cautiously. Slurry loses a lot of its volume as the excess water drains out of it, and the next day my form was only 1/3 full. On the second day I filled the form 3/4 full, and the next morning it was about half full. Not until the third day did I completely fill the form to the top with slurry.

One thing I quickly learned is that concrete blocks are inadequate to withstand the pressure of the slurry, so the bottom of my form bulged out a bit. Also, despite the linseed oil, the plywood warped. After this experience, I decided to saw the plywood in half, creating two forms that were 8 feet long and only 2 feet high. This proved to be a much more manageable size, and I decided to pour my entire perimeter wall with these forms.

Here's a view looking right down the middle of the form to the bottom. If the bottom of the form bows inward, you merely have to saw a piece of 1x2 to the width of your

wall and insert it into the bottom of the form before putting the form into place. The spacer block will be surrounded by slurry, and will become a permanent part of the wall.

Here's one of my "half size" forms full of slurry. You will notice that I hadn't talked to Eric Patterson yet, so I was still using a "plastic foundation." On the bottom-right of the picture is a little papercrete retaining wall I poured, to keep dirt away from the wall of the office. Notice that I was now using three top braces rather than two, to prevent excess bowing at the top of the form. Also, I was using stakes driven into the ground to keep the bottom of the form from bowing. To avoid stability problems, I filled the form only 2/3 full on the first day, not topping it off until the next day.

The section of wall shown in the previous picture is now completed, and the form has been moved to its new position.

After the 2-foot-high perimeter wall segments had been poured, I decided to use 8-foot-long 2x8s as forms for the remainder of the wall. Since these forms were 11" wide (outside dimension) and only 7½" tall, there was no danger of them tipping over, and they could simply rest on top of 3/8" steel rods laid across the previously-poured wall.

Down in the bottom-right corner, this closeup shows a 3/8" steel rod, 12" long, that serves as support for the 2x8 form. Three of these rods are adequate for an 8-foot-long form; I use two of them for a shorter length. After the slurry has set up and the form has been removed, the steel rods are pulled out of the wall, leaving small holes that will automatically be covered over when the wall is plastered inside and out.

In the next photo I pour slurry from a bucket into a 2x8 form. The higher the wall became, the more work was involved. There is a tradeoff when pouring slurry directly into forms like this. On one hand, you eliminate the block-making process entirely, but on the other hand you've got to lift all that wet slurry into position. Dry or semi-dry blocks, with less moisture content, are much easier to lift than buckets of wet slurry.

There is a further disadvantage to using forms—you are constantly adding wet slurry to the top of the wall, which keeps the already-poured lower sections soaking wet. The wall doesn't really have a chance to dry out until the last section is finally poured at the very top.

Furthermore, with a skinny 8"-wide wall like mine, the heavy, wet slurry at the top makes the wall top-heavy and potentially unstable. This would be much less of a concern with a standard 12" wall. I decided to make an 8" wall for 3 reasons: (1) I have a very small building spot and wanted literally every extra inch of inside space I could; (2) Unlike a

home, which needs to handle continuous human habitation, this office would be occupied for only several hours a day, and presumably could get by with "only" an R-24 wall; (3) I would have to mix only 200 loads of slurry rather than 300.

After filling the form with slurry, I smooth off the top with a trowel, as shown in the previous photo. The slurry that slops onto the top of the form is a valuable resource—after it dries, I peel it off in strips and save it. Since slurry shrinks as it dries, the form is always slightly wider than the partially-dried wall beneath it. I use the strips of dried slurry to seal off any large gaps between the form and the wall. It's amazing, though, how well slurry will plug even a 3/4" gap. You would think that it would ooze right on through, but it just hangs up in there and only the excess water flows out.

This is how our office looked in mid-September 1998, and it remained this way until the following April, when Greg Jay came upon the scene and spent 3 months papercreting with me. We, with a lot of help from our workshop participants, finished the rest of the wall with blocks. As of this writing (August 1999) the roof is completed, and the floor of the top room is about 3/4 finished. This fall, or whenever we can find some spare time, we hope to get this building completed.

Silver City Update

This is the foundation system I decided to use after talking to Eric Patterson. First, using a 2x4 form, I pour a little foundation on the ground, whose main purpose is getting the bottom of the wall 3 1/2" off the ground. On top of the foundation is a piece of black plastic to prevent water from wicking up into the wall, and a piece of roof edge along the outside of the foundation, which will be plastered over when the building is completed. When pouring the foundation, I inserted wire loops every couple of feet. The end of each loop sticks straight up into the air, as is shown in the lower-right corner of this photo. Other pieces of wire are tied onto the wire loops as the wall is built. This wire will continue all the way up to the top of the wall, and will be used to anchor the roof plate to the foundation. It would be easier to embed steel or plastic strapping in the foundation, and tie down the roof plates that way.

When we visited Eric Patterson this past spring, he took us to a house in Silver City where he built a 200-foot perimeter wall out of papercrete three years ago. It was built using slip forms. Except for some minor cracking, the wall is holding up very well, and the owner is very happy with it.

80

Recent Paper Adobe Experiments at City of the Sun

We visited City of the Sun, near Columbus, NM, several times this spring, to shoot some footage for our video, and to see what Sean Sands and Mike McCain are up to these days. In addition to experimenting with paper adobe, Mike is working on his "roamer," an innovative new bicycle design, and Sean is still hard at work building experimental, ultra low cost structures out of dirt, paper, and bottles.

This year Sean is using a tow mixer, designed and built by Mike McCain. He is using it in stationary mode, and is powering it with the same wrecked pickup truck he was using last year. His cost breakdown is as follows: $150 for the truck, $50 for the stock tank, $50 for the automotive rear axle, and $1 for the lawnmower blade, which they bought on sale.

Here's another view of the mixer. In the background is some of Sean's accumulation of blocks he made last year. Sean says it takes about 20 minutes to mix up a load of paper pulp this way. He puts dry newspapers and magazines into the tank, fills the tank with water, and starts mixing. The mixer doesn't have to be tended, so he can be working at other tasks while the batch is mixing. He says that such a mixer would be ideal for a community, since this mixer is large enough to handle several different projects at once.

Sean is making paper adobe this year. He uses the mixer to make paper pulp. To make paper adobe, he takes one bucket of paper pulp out of the mixer and puts it in a wheelbarrow, adds one bucket of dirt from on-site (he estimates that it has a 30% clay content), and mixes them together with a hoe.

He sees no reason why he can't get the cost for materials down to **zero**.

As we mentioned last issue, Sean's unfinished, unsealed domes collapsed after absorbing an enormous amount of rainwater after some heavy rains last summer. He decided to rebuild the largest of his domes, using paper adobe mortar rather than papercrete mortar. The paper adobe mortar is stickier than papercrete, adheres very well to the papercrete blocks, and doesn't pull away from the blocks when it dries. This view shows the top of his dome, with a rainwater channel sculpted out of paper adobe.

The top of the dome was covered with a sheet of 6-mil polyethylene, which was then covered with a couple of inches of paper adobe, to prevent the plastic from disintegrating in the sunlight. The paper adobe was sealed with linseed oil mixed 50/50 with paint thinner. Sean is intrigued with the possibility of using canola oil as a roof sealer, because it is much cheaper than linseed oil.

This is a solar collector on the south side of the dome. You can tell it's a solar collector, because he used all clear bottles, not green or brown. The sunlight penetrates the bottles, and heats the surface of the dome, which serves as a Trombe wall.

Sean likes to build with bottles. They are free, plentiful, strong, and easy to work with. They create a beautiful stained glass effect when the sun shines through them.

Sean built a spiral entryway into the dome, using papercrete blocks left over from last year, mortared together with paper adobe.

Here's an overview of Sean's experimental building projects. The dome, with spiral entryway, is at the lower-right corner.

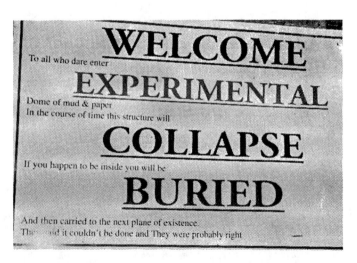

WELCOME
To all who dare enter
EXPERIMENTAL
Dome of mud & paper
In the course of time this structure will
COLLAPSE
If you happen to be inside you will be
BURIED
And then carried to the next plane of existence.
They said it couldn't be done and They were probably right

Sean's building projects are not recommended for the narrow-minded, or faint of heart.

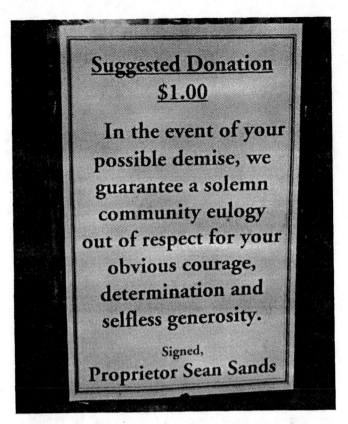

Warning sign inside Sean's dome.

This is Sean and Esther's outdoor bath house. A roofless adobe privacy wall is open to the sky. A cast iron bathtub sits on top of a firebox. A fire is built under the tub, and smoke exits out the stovepipe. What could be simpler, or more elegant?

This house will look familiar to people who have read EQ #1. Sean has covered the house with paper adobe mortar.

A neighbor's greenhouse dramatically shows the difference between papercrete and paper adobe mortar. On the left, the papercrete shows a lot of cracking. The paper adobe on the right is free of cracks.

83

Here Sean applies mortar to the roof of the house shown in the previous picture. He is experimenting with using prickly pear mucilage as a sealing agent. The inside of a prickly pear cactus pad (or its close relative, cholla cactus) is filled with slimy pulp which has traditionally been used as a sealer. This usually requires boiling and/or fermentation to remove the mucilage from the pulp.

Since Sean has a 200-gallon mixer, which is essentially a huge kitchen blender, he decided to run the pads through the mixer to remove the mucilage. First, he gathered a bunch of prickly pear pads from the surrounding desert. He harvested only 1-2 pads off of each plant, to cause minimal environmental damage and ensure a sustainable harvest. Then he filled the mixer 3/4 full of prickly pear pads and water, and blended them together. Then he strained the glop through a 1/2" screen to remove the bigger pieces.

Then, using a wheelbarrow and a hoe, he mixes together a bucket of the mucilage with a bucket of dry adobe dirt. This makes a goo which he applies by hand (wearing rubber gloves), and then trowels smooth. The "cactus mortar" becomes surprisingly hard when dry, and he is considering using this formula for floors as well as roofs. He emphasizes that this, along with his other building innovations, is an experiment, and that time will tell if it holds up to the elements.

Mike McCain welded together this steel drag form for

making paper adobe blocks. He calls paper adobe **fidobe**— short for "fibrous adobe."

Another view of his drag form.

The drag form creates long ribbons of fidobe which Mike cuts into blocks with this shovel. He welded a spacer onto the shovel so that he could cut uniform blocks.

Crestone Update

We received some photos from Kelly Hart of Crestone, CO, showing his new papercrete mixer and his earthbag home that he has covered with papercrete stucco. Here are his photos and accompanying letter:

I want to let the EQ readers know how pleased I am with the "tow mixer" for making papercrete. After working with the 55 gallon electric mixer quite a bit, this new mixer is a dream. It will make 4-6 times as much at a time with less effort; it will pulp almost any kind of paper without pre-soaking (although I do usually soak magazines and catalogs to make it easier on the machine); it will make a mix so thick it has to be shoveled rather than drained out. All you have to do is put the ingredients in the mixer and drive around the block, and it's ready to use!

Mike McCain helped me select the rear axle and he did the initial welding, while I completed the assembly of the machine. We chose a low ratio (2:1) rear end so that there is less drag when pulling with our Volvo station wagon. Even at this ratio I need to drive as slowly as I can, especially at first. I made a couple of modifications to Mike's basic design. First, I made a heavy wooden lid so that the mix doesn't slop out so much when you start mixing. Second, I created a tripod feature so that the whole mixer can be tilted up with the tong pointing up in the air, and it will rest in that position. Whenever I'm not using the mixer I store it in this position so that the heavy oil in the axle will lubricate the part of the rear end that is usually attached to the drive line of the car. Several tow mixers have seized up after a few months of use, I suspect because of lack of lubrication to the part that is attached to the blade.

Here's a photo of me applying the papercrete to the outside of the large sandbag dome. I was rushing to get it covered before the snows fly (we live at 8000 feet in Colorado).

I did manage to get it enclosed just a few days before the world turned white.

—Kelly Hart

A $154 Papercrete Guest House

We recently received some photographs from Jacque Zaleski of WindTree Ranch, showing how, for a cost of $104, they converted a pickup truck camper shell that they bought for $50 at an auction into a snug, well-insulated, guest cottage. Captions are by Jacque Zaleski. For more information about WindTree Ranch and their papercrete workshops, write them at RR 2 Box 1, Douglas, AZ 85607-9802, or e-mail them at: <windtreeranch@theriver.com>. Web site: <www.windtree.org>.

First block is up!

$50 camper on free oak pallets stuffed with free dirt—Don added a basement, too (see black metal box in lower level).

Building a "free" stone wall with mortar two layers deep to support papercrete blocks—we painted camper before work began.

Blocks begin to cover camper—note doors and window bucks. New screens, too. Interior was remodeled.

Papercrete roof! New skylight is also on.

Stucco and "one coat" mix—both dyed to match landscape.

EXPENSES

Camper bought at auction -- $50. We later sold the full propane tank for $30 and the propane stove top for $10, so our net cost for the camper was $10.

2'-3' tall rock foundation
    rocks -- free
    mortar -- $12

120 6"x12"x6" papercrete blocks required 4 bags Portland
    cement -- $24

mortar for blocks -- $18

stucco -- 2 coats

2½ bags cement -- $15
2½ bags "Western One Coat" -- $30
5 boxes cement dye -- $11

1 quart paint -- free

door buck & skylight & window bucks
    one 4x8' sheet of ½" plywood -- $7
    one 16-foot 2x8 -- $10

salvaged plexiglass -- free

new window screens -- $6

4 oak pallets -- free

Roof
    1 mixer load of papercrete = 1 bag cement -- $6
    coat of asphalt emulsion -- $8
    limestone gravel over wet asphalt -- free
    rammed earth -- free

Plumbing
    3/4" pipe -- $3

TOTAL $154

A nice guest house for $154. What do you think?

87

LETTERS

I'm concerned about using tar to waterproof these paper-fibrous cement houses. The rain coming off a tar roof is brown or amber colored because the tar leaches into it. The same is true of tar paper, rolled tar composition paper, and composition shingles. Many of us will want to harvest this run-off, and in any event such water will contaminate the soil around a house. A better product to use on the top of a fibrous cement house might be the white or cream-colored grout or goop used to seal cracks in swimming pools. Perhaps other readers can comment on this. I've used such grout to seal my concrete bird baths, and it lasts for years and years.

Chuck Ouray
Edgewood, NM

I would very much like doing a 1 room fibrous cement building this summer, but preferably not a dome—metal roofs work well here with our snow. Lots of questions though—I was wondering if a cement mixer could be used—we have one.

Louise Pape
Soaring Eagle Ranch
Los Ojos, NM

A cement mixer can be used, particularly if the paper is shredded first. However, there are 3 main problems using a cement mixer for mixing fibrous cement: (1) the capacity is too small, (2) the speed is too slow, and (3) the paddles are not designed for cutting paper. Adding about a dozen fist-sized rocks or 3" diameter steel ball bearings will help. A mixer specifically designed for the task will do a much better job.

We are very psyched to build our next project with fibrous cement blocks. We have already talked about doing that, having heard of Eric Patterson's project in Silver City, and also having met Bill Knauss in Tucson, who is experimenting with paper adobe (no cement, straw added mostly for texture). He uses a paddle-type mortar mixer and throws in dry paper, clay, water and straw. But I think I like the method you

showed Sean Sands using best. Mike McCain's looked a bit too large-scale for us.

Harry Browne
Pinos Altos, NM

I made a test batch of fibrous cement in the wife's blender this afternoon. Thank God she was not here and I did not have to ask permission to put some cement in her blender. Aside from a messy kitchen it looks very successful at this point.

Allen Gooch
Arlington, TX

We are quite intrigued with fibrous cement—what a great use for scrap paper! We've been talking for years about building a sauna—so, the bags of paper have been transferred from the recycling bin to the sauna materials spot. The challenge of building for the colder north will keep us happily busy for awhile!

Sue Robishaw
Cooks, MI

I am very excited about the possibilities of fibrous cement. I am currently moving onto my homestead (40 acres west of Pueblo, Colo.)—there is a shell of a wood framed house which we will be moving into, but as we have virtually no money, I have been very concerned about how to build the interior walls (everything currently just studs in plywood sheathing) & how to afford insulation. Fibrous cement might just answer my desperate calls for help. Plus, it sounds ideal for the addition to the house which we were planning on building with cob.

Trina Clemente
Pueblo, CO

We sure are stirred up about fibrous cement structures. I do believe we will give it a serious attempt.

Meg Koeppen
Arivaca, AZ

Have been in a quandary—needing to build studio space but losing my income source for the summer. Fibrous cement sounds like just what I'm needing—well, that and a good ole boy

with stock tank, lawnmower blade, and a V8 (grin).

Alice Q. Swanson
Old Joe, AR

We have never been able to afford building to code so our housing has been of poor quality. So the reality and vision of working with a low cost, strong, accessible material like fibrous cement is wonderful and exciting. It may provide a solution.

Chester McQueary
Parachute, CO

The concept of light, insulating, strong, cheap, easy to make/use fibrous cement is an idea whose time has come.

R.B. Minton
Raton, NM

I am thrilled with the paper house article. I am dreaming of making paper cement sculpture—sand and/or earth casting—garden goddesses/fountains—rainbows—and boats—what about boats?

Sunny Warner
Tucson, AZ

For sculptures, Eric Patterson recommends adding Elmer's glue to the slurry—it then dries to a hard consistency that can be sanded to give a smooth finish. As for boats, fibrous cement/papercrete absorbs water like a sponge. If a boat was painted inside and out with several coats of silicone sealer, it might work.

The fibrous cement information in **Earth Quarterly** caught my interest. So I rummaged in the storage shed and found a food processor at the bottom of the "stuff." Raced inside and tore up some newspaper. Then I remembered I needed cement and sand. Sand I had none, but a friend had some post hole cement and I strained out the rocks and had a cupful or so in the bottom of a 5 gallon pail. In the house I estimated I could put about a quart of water in the processor, which I did, turned it on and added the paper. Well, I found out that the processor has a very limited space for water. It was flowing over the inside, water was splashing everywhere.

So I did what every red blooded American would do, I decreased the

88

water amount. Then to my amazement, the processor is designed to lift the material upward, and nothing was happening. So I took a wooden spoon handle and gently pushed the paper downward. At the same time I was trying to reach the 5 gallon pail to scoop out a couple tablespoons of cement, the processor became so unbalanced that it started rocking back and forth so violently that I spilt most of the cement. After a bit with cement and water splashed everywhere, I poured it into a mold. I liked what the result was. So I have since built a 55 gallon mixer and several forms.

Bill Harvey
Payson, AZ

Fibrous cement has to be the most ingenious, exciting idea to come along yet! Imagine building practically free! For years, this 64-year-old displaced homemaker has thought about building a home. However, with very little fixed income—how can it be done? Now I know!

Betty McGee
Vardaman, MS

Your focus on fibrous cement was both excellent and inspiring. Makes me want to go into production tomorrow!

C.R. Cheney
Summertown, TN

The depth of your article on "Paper Houses" was outstanding... just what I was hoping to see in print so that the world can get exposed to the otherwise unbelievable reality these homes offer. Thanks for all the hard work/planning that goes into publishing such an incredible wealth of information.

Robert Paulson
Golden, CO

I was planning to buy a farm in Missouri and build either a straw bale, cordwood, or Geo-dome kit home. Now it will be fibrous cement. In an old issue of *Mother Earth News*, they had the plans for a building "hoop" anchored on pins at both ends that let you build a big cordwood dome. This would work great on fibrous cement.

Truss work can be 1-2 feet wide.

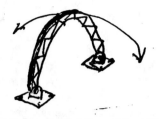

You just lay the brick and "mud" them in place and after drying time, winch the truss forward to the next course to be laid. Truss design allows for small to big 40' high domes.

Keep up the good work. You have jump started my brain.

Bob Carnes
Cullowhee, NC

I'm planning on building a house with alternative techniques. I was set on straw-bale and cob, but the paper house looks great! Maybe I'll combine all three and throw in a tire patio wall... name the house the Earth Loving Mutt.

Joseph Birkett
Arivaca, AZ

Just had to write and let you know I saw your ad "Paper Brick Houses 75¢/sq. foot" in the *Mother Earth News*. When I saw the ad I thought to myself, "yeah, right" and decided to "waste the $3.00 to see what kind of scam it was.

I am an elderly woman who lives alone on 40 acres. I have no electricity, running water, etc. I have been reading books on alternative housing, trying to find a method I can handle to build myself a house.

Most of the methods I have read about require what I call the "3 M's" (money-muscle-machinery) all of which I have in very limited quantities. Then came your ad.

This is the best $3.00 I ever "wasted." I believe I've found a method I can handle to build myself a house. Thank you.

Karren Lay
Dove Creek, CO

I am excited and impressed with your publication. Folks have completely lost touch with sound inexpensive shelter! They are brainwashed into paying 30 year mortgages on wooden stick homes. This is pretty damn lost! Folks just accept huge debt as part of the homeowner experience. This lacks

vision and, to be frank, common sense! I am very interested in all effective inexpensive Earth building modes. Keep your light shining.

Josh Logan
Lakewood, CO

Fibrous cement looks to be a great idea—I wonder if it would work as an insulating stucco mixture over the exterior of a tire house? Only one way to find out!

David Stebbins
Canyon, TX

I bet fibrous cement would work great as insulating stucco!

I only used caliche one time in my very first FC mixture. That's because I had some "screenings" left over from the flooring project in the goat barn. Everything mixed up afterwards has been made with builders sand. The mix with caliche didn't have the paper pulped up enough, either. So the resultant mix was nonconsistent and weak. It won't even hold a screw.

Actually the best results I'm having are with the basic 6,3,1 ratio using sand. Then, instead of just pouring it into a mold and letting it ripen, I "pack" it. This is just patting it with your hand until the top is smooth and it has shrunk in thickness somewhat. When a piece of this is dry, it will hold a screw really well. It still won't hold a straight nail (just pull and it's out) but it did hold a 1/4" eye bolt. My husband wiggled it back and forth, trying to imitate the action of wind... it gave a tiny bit but still held. Looks like this is the usual results. So, nothing new there.

I do have some test pieces drying using a 6,3,2 ratio. If it goes like I hope, then I'll use this mix as mortar and roofing material. I'm looking for increased strength and brittleness to withstand both shear in the walls and bouncing hail on the roof.

I will probably try another mix using caliche but not until I have my mixing machine. When I do try the caliche screenings, caliche "sand" and small 1/4" pebbles, I'll certainly let you know how it comes out.

Mary S. Miller
Poolville, TX

After reading your article on papercrete I am ready to begin building! The photo essay was superb and one of the best I've seen or read on any topic. I felt like you had indeed, successfully communicated the necessary information for this building process. (No small feat!)

I like the fiber cement method for many reasons. One of the best reasons is the lightweight nature of this mix! Working with 15 lb. blocks is about what I can handle as long as the pace is s-l-o-w!

William Lloyd Kelley
Flagstaff, AZ

Your article on fibrous cement was the most interesting building article I've read in a long while, and I've read a lot.

Jim Graham
Las Cruces, NM

The paper cement info seems very helpful. I wonder whether it will do well in the harsh Indiana winter?

Bill Fennell
Laporte, IN

Considering that unsealed papercrete roofs stand up to the heavy snow loads of a Colorado winter, I would think that a properly designed papercrete building, on a dry foundation and sealed from the elements, would perform well just about anywhere.

I've become very enthused about the potentials of fibrous cement. Not only do I envision my husband & myself building with it (he has already cleared out a shed for storing paper) but I see it as possibly useful for other projects as well. Specifically, I have built several bat houses out of wood which have not successfully attracted bats. I have been hoping for a material which would insulate better, as well as being much lighter so they'd be easier to put up. Construction of bat houses with fibrous cement could be much simpler & less time-consuming as well.

However, the issue of mixers does slow down our enthusiasm a bit, as it sounds like it does with other people.

I have had some experience with making paper as art. Artists, of course, have had to deal with some of these problems for years, and people with a lot of background in this could be good resources. Papermaking classes, for instance, have to produce large amounts of pulp for students. At the University of MN (Mlps.) the papermaking studio was equipped with a <u>Hollander beater</u>, a large, round trough-like piece of equipment which probably costs a mint but could produce sufficient pulp for a small brick-making operation. Perhaps Hollander makes other size equipment as well, or would at least be a good resource.

As far as other problems, such as waterproofing materials, I remember in an early workshop adding vinyl wallpaper paste (powder, comes in a bag) to the pulp for some of my pieces. This definitely made a sturdier piece of art. I'm not up on all the newest developments in papermaking technology but again, working artists might have experience that could apply to paper architecture. I know there are working papermakers in Albuquerque; possibly UNM even has a papermaking dept.

Thanks for all the great work you're doing!

Ann E. Schmidt
Winslow, AZ

I discovered your web site, and am intrigued! I have some land in central Arizona, and have been considering cob, straw bale, geodesic domes, and, most recently, monolithic concrete domes. Now you've got me thinking about using fibrous cement in place of shotcrete in a monolithic dome.

Greg Carter
Petaluma, CA

My friend and I work and live on the Hopi Reservation in the Four Corners area. We spoke briefly about your magazines and the papercrete process with Laura at the Alternative Energy Fair in Flagstaff a few weeks back. It was late Sunday, my friend had three dollars and I five, so we each bought the issue of **Earth Quarterly** we could afford at that moment. Maybe that will trigger an association...

Even though attendance at the Fair was disappointing, please know you profoundly affected at least a couple of people who came to your booth. I speak of Preston and myself, as we now feel papercrete may be the building material we have spent years looking for. We are doing separate projects, but papercrete appears to have universal application.

Preston is currently remodeling a stone house in which he lives in one of the Hopi villages. He sees papercrete as a viable method for adding a lightweight second floor to the structure he is currently enlarging. In my situation, I am at foundation level building a cabin on forty acres of high desert land an hour west of Flagstaff. I was doing slip-form stone, but now plan to stop at eighteen inches above ground level with the stone and complete the structure with papercrete walls. I mention these projects as potential subject matter for future articles for **Earth Quarterly**.

I wish to say thank you for "being out there." What you are doing is very important.

Ed Taylor
Williams, AZ

We are very excited about the paper blocks as a building material. We have no way of recycling junk mail, magazines, and a lot of other paper products in our county so being able to keep this waste paper out of the landfill (where it forms between 30 to 45% of the volume), and turn it into a superior and cheap building material, sounds wonderful to me. I am currently vice-chair of the Cochise County Task Force for Solid Waste Alternatives so am eager to find ways to reduce what goes into the landfills.

We had been planning to build a straw bale wall, 20 feet out from our house, to create more outdoor living space by blocking the winter cold or drying summer winds and create a microclimate for plantings and gardening. But the paper blocks sound like a much cheaper, lighter, and easier way to go. Straw is $6 a bale here. So thank you for your efforts in getting the word out so that we could hear about it.

Valerie McCaffrey
Elfrida, AZ

I'm on my way to Russia & Malaysia for business meetings, then to Missouri to buy my farm and get on with the project of experimenting with "papercrete." Really enjoyed your #2 issue.

Once I get going, I'll share all my detailed drawings & etc. so people can go to a local wrecking yard and welding shop and have a home or commercial size mixer, moulder, sizer/cutter and forms made. I'll make it an easy project for beginners.

Years ago, Sears sold cement molds for 3-4 different type blocks so a person could build their own "stone look-alike home"... no reason this can't be done with paper blocks.

You may want to try a waterproofing material called XYPEX. It is made by XYPEX Chemical Corporation. It seals concrete through a crystallization process. For sales & tech support call 888-443-7922. Website: www.hi-dry.com. This product (cost I do not know) followed by your Homestar sealer might just prove a great exterior coating.

God bless you good people for all the hard work.

Bob Carnes
Asheboro, NC

We are presently building a straw-bale cottage & were really excited by the article on "fibrous cement." Of course we wonder how it would hold up in Canadian conditions! We look forward to lots of alternative building & lifestyle news.

Joan Chadwick
Tappan, BC, Canada

I've not been making many blocks. Have been working on a simple pump for moving the mixture faster than a shovel and pail. When I have the bugs worked out will send pictures and such.

Bill Harvey
Payson, AZ

I read your **Earth Quarterlies** cover to cover and loved all the info on papercrete. I am excited about it because it sounds like something I could do myself. Light weight and all that. I have one question, if there is water damage at the ground line, what solutions are they coming up with.

Linda Drew
Tucson, AZ

Papercrete is of particular interest to women, because the blocks can be made as small as you choose to handle. And now, with the new information we have about small, garbage disposal mixers, papercrete is more feasible for everybody. There are two schools of thought about foundations: (1) build your wall on a concrete foundation with a moisture barrier to prevent wicking, or (2) build your wall on a rubble trench so that rainwater will go down into the trench rather up into the wall. There are so few paper houses built so far, it's too early to say which, or both, of these methods is preferable. Time will tell.

Concerning lime/versus cement: the main reason is that lime gives a quality to the air breathed inside a house that cement not only doesn't - retains moisture - lime exhales it maintaining indoor hydro content drier.

And cement - at least in Latin Europe - can carry toxic and/or radioactive components. Lime has been manufactured with a very simple technology - 5000 years ago they were already making lime in the Mediterranean countries.

Emilia Hazelip
Limoux-Cedex, France

I feel like **Earth Quarterly** is on the "cutting edge" of living well on the planet. I am trying to work out a fiber cement mixer that will be built with easily available materials. With a standardized plan that anyone could follow.

I plan to build a fiber cement home. The gods willing I will have a good plan by April with some excess casholas, TO BEGIN the foundation for this thing. I plan to rubble the footing and then "slip" the foundation wall. It shouldn't take too long to do. I am going to try to heat the structure with the sun.

William Kelley
Flagstaff, AZ

Re: your papercrete mixer: as a contractor for many years, I had occasion to witness what unprotected v-belts and pulleys can do to fingers (takes 'em right off... you're much better off using a skillsaw). I would LOVE to see the belt and pulley atop your mixer covered to prevent tools or fingers from getting into the wrong spot. I think it would be an excellent idea to mention the covering in a future issue of the magazine, for the protection both of your readers and yourselves. Good design work, by the way—simple and effective. With the belt-and-pulley cover added, it's perfect!

Keep up the great work, and thanks for putting the magazine together!

Jack Rowe
College Station, TX

Thanks for sending us this valuable advice.

It was a delight to receive your **Earth Quarterly**. I was grabbed in 4th grade with the idea of making houses from recycled materials when my dad brought home cardboard boxes which became my fort. Over the years I've worked on a lot of ideas—mostly mentally. I would love to connect with some other people thinking along these lines to especially eventually form a community that would include gardens, recreation, homemade, handmade, houses. Also, where o where is it permissible to build? So many places have such stringent codes, one cannot wiggle! I'd love to hear from any of your readers thinking along these veins.

I love the **Earth Quarterlies**! Thanks for manifesting a wonderful concept.

Kristi Cadwell
Richland, WA

Even today, there are rural counties that don't make a fetish of building codes. A good way to find out would be to stop at the most unusual house you can find and ask the owner what he/she did about codes.

I am going to apply fibrous cement over a dome form, and then remove the dome. I'll let you know how it goes.

Terry Lee
Cedar Crest, NM

Please send me issues 1 and 2. We are a small community in eastern Montana looking to recycle our paper somehow. Right now we are too far from everything to make most recycling projects break even, much less pay. Thanks.

Bruce Smith
Dawson County Extension Agent
Glendive, MT

I am stuccoing the exterior of my tire house with (drum roll, please)... Fibrous Cement! It adheres to the tires very well. You'll be interested in how I'm making my FC. I shred up newspapers (I got 500 pounds free from a printer who is interested in what I'm doing... I gave him a copy of EQ #1 as a gift) using a leaf whacker (Sears, on sale for $99) and mix up the shredded paper in a little cement mixer (Harbor Freight, $200) with portland cement, water and sand. Works good. The leaf whacker is not great as a high volume shredder (it gets kind of overwhelmed unless you feed it real slow), but it works, and I can make FC using off-the-shelf products pretty cheap, and I can also shred leaves (not that we have a surplus of leaves in the Texas Panhandle) and/or mix cement when I need to, using the same tools I use to make FC. If I was building a house with FC, I'd build a dedicated machine, but for stucco, I think I can get by with the stuff I've got.

David Stebbins
Canyon, TX

Your publication is a godsend—especially the articles on "papercrete"! I've built the mixer, tried several different forms, and am still experimenting with different ratios of clay, sand and cement to paper. I have one question for you though: all of your papercrete articles call for shovels full of "cement," but do you mean the prepackaged cement that has aggregate in it, mortar-type cement, or Portland cement. I have been using "post hole" cement that I had left over from another

project, and the rocks rip up the mixer blade and sink to the bottom.

Maryruth Monahan
End of the Line Ranch
Ash Fork, AZ

Please forgive the oversight—I should have specified "Portland cement."

I received issues #1 & 2 of **Earth Quarterly** & was very impressed. I'm 41 & been in home building & remodeling most all my life. I hope to be leaving Ohio fairly soon & was gona move back out west somewhere. I went to school in Deming & also lived in Las Cruces & because I'm so interested in this "fibrous cement" I've decided to move back to that area. I look forward to meeting & working with you & others to improve & work with this product. Keep up the good work & open mind!

Scott Childress
Orient, OH

Just borrowed 1st issue of **Earth Quarterly**—awesome! I've seen one dome built from papercrete. We are building a mixer and going to really promote this idea here.

Also, many large companies—especially news organizations—have bins & bins of shredded paper cut back—glad to have someone haul it away!

Hawk
Arivaca, AZ

Here's how I make papercrete stucco for my tire house: I use a shortened edger blade on a 1/2 inch drill. The paper is shredded first in a leaf wacker. I dump a couple of pounds (?) or so of the shredded paper into a 55-gallon barrel that's been cut in half, add about five gallons of water, add three shovel fulls of portland cement, two of sand, a couple tablespoons of air entrainment, and mix for five or ten minutes with the drill/edger blade. Makes a good stucco mix. I realize I use quite a bit of portland, but the

stucco is just an inch thick and I need the strength. Also, I feel it makes the mix more fire retardant.

David Stebbins
Canyon, TX

My heart leaped when I received your special "Paper House" issue of **Earth Quarterly**. I've worked for years trying to devise a way to make homes from recycled materials that would be functional & beautiful. You definitely filled in some blanks for me & I am thankful to you. Best wishes as you continue to build these wonderful houses.

Kristi Cadwell
Richland, WA

I'm planning to build a timber-fibrous concrete house. In spite of its cheapness, the qualities of f.c. are outstanding. And the component materials are mostly environmentally correct to boot. Thanks a lot.

Clarence Ching
Kamuela, HI

Do you know if anyone has experimented with using gypsum (plaster of paris) instead of cement in papercrete? There is a man doing this with earth and pumping this directly into forms for walls for houses. If you're interested, here is the site address: <www.castearth.com>.

Paul Sarnstrom
hoh@rmi.net

I wonder if papercrete floats? Has anyone tried making a hull out of it and sealed it for launching? There are ferro-cement boats out there that are strong and still sailing. Just a thought, albeit a weird one!

Marcus Bachino
Williams, OR

Unsealed papercrete absorbs water like a sponge. If you thoroughly sealed a papercrete boat with silicone, it should float. I'm not sure if I would trust the sealer to keep the boat from eventually sinking, however.

Conclusion

Laura and I have been seriously involved with papercrete for a little over a year now, and it's interesting to note how, on the one hand, the papercrete movement is evolving so rapidly, and on the other hand, how it's barely begun.

The modern papercrete movement began, as far as we can tell, back in 1983 with James Moon's papercrete domes in Tucson. He set up a company and ambitiously promoted his innovative design concepts, evidently without much success. Eric Patterson of Silver City, NM, was featured in a documentary that was broadcast over PBS, and he estimates that he has had 1000 visitors over the years. Mike McCain has built papercrete structures in Colorado and New Mexico, and gives occasional papercrete workshops. Sean Sands gets a dozen or two visitors each week coming to see his papercrete and paper adobe houses. **Earth Quarterly** has been promoting papercrete as heavily as possible for the past year. Yet I will bet that most of the people who are reading this had never heard of papercrete until they encountered this book. It just goes to show you how vast this world really is, and how difficult it is to make any kind of impact.

The present papercrete movement is at about the same place the straw bale movement was in 1990—very few people know about it, and the concept sounds downright weird to a lot of people. Back then it was "Build a house with straw? You gotta be kidding!" But a few people caught the vision and persevered with it, and today straw bale houses are commonplace. The same thing is sure to happen with papercrete and paper adobe. It's an idea whose time will surely come.

I need to emphasize once again that papercrete and paper adobe are **experimental** at this time. There are no guarantees at this point. Personally, I think that people who don't seal their papercrete roofs and exterior stucco will be in for a surprise several years down the line, when their roofs and walls start to disintegrate. This is why I recommend a conservative approach—a high and dry foundation, a roof with plenty of overhang, and walls that are thoroughly sealed from the elements. A papercrete house built to these specifications should last indefinitely, and will be strong, well-insulated, and very inexpensive. .

The big change I've noticed in the past year has been a new emphasis on paper adobe. Bill Knauss of Tucson started experimenting with it several years ago, and now both Sean Sands and Mike McCain are working with paper adobe exclusively. Paper adobe has a couple of advantages over papercrete—**Earth-friendliness** (cement production releases a lot of carbon dioxide into the atmosphere, and uses a lot of fossil fuels both in production and transportation to the job site, whereas dirt is a much more environmentally benign substance) and **low cost** (suitable dirt is often available free, on-site).

Paper adobe also has several advantages over regular adobe (or rammed earth, or cob)—for starters, **increased insulation value** (regular dirt is a poor insulator, and adding paper fibers and air pockets to the mix is very beneficial) and **lower weight** (If you have ever laid adobe blocks, you know how much brutal hard work is involved. Paper adobe blocks are much lighter in weight than regular adobe, and won't wear you out as quickly).

Mike McCain says that unlike regular adobe, paper adobe can be painted. You just brush the excess dirt off the surface of the block, exposing the paper fibers. The paint is absorbed by the paper fibers, and doesn't flake off like it would if you painted regular adobe.

Another advantage of paper adobe over regular adobe is it doesn't disintegrate in the rain the way that regular adobe does. Each drop of rain falling from a high altitude has a considerable impact... and rain, over a period of years, will gradually erode away unprotected adobe. With paper adobe, the paper fibers offer protection from erosion, and unprotected paper adobe blocks stand up to the elements quite well.

One exciting advantage of paper adobe is that fact that **paper adobe looks like regular adobe**. This is an important psychological factor which can be used to advantage when dealing with building inspectors. Papercrete dries to a gray color, and looks like, well, papercrete. You can rap on a cured papercrete block and it rings like a block of wood and is obviously quite strong, but **it looks unfamiliar**. People who encounter a papercrete block for the first time pick it up and say, "What is this?" There is no instant recognition, no point of reference. People are always skeptical of something new until they become familiar with it.

There is much less of that skepticism with paper adobe. Paper adobe is brown, and looks like regular adobe. Only its relatively light weight gives it away. Frankly, I suspect that building inspectors (especially those who are already familiar with adobe) will not have too many problems with paper adobe, as long as it passes their compression tests (which it will). I think it will be relatively easy for building inspectors to view paper adobe as "enhanced adobe"—adobe with a higher fiber content than usual. Approving paper adobe won't be quite as psychologically difficult as approving a totally new substance like papercrete.

Apart from building codes, the papercrete movement's biggest obstacle is the necessity of building mixers. This is an intimidating prospect for most people. Even though there is a guaranteed demand for papercrete and paper adobe blocks, there is nobody, to our knowledge, producing them at this time. Travis Coffey's factory, as described on pages 28-31 of this book, is on hold. The only other person I know of who has the ability, money, and determination to produce papercrete blocks commercially is Bill Knauss of Tucson. He is interested in forming a land trust somewhere in the Southwest and starting an alternative economic system, with a paper block factory as a key part of this plan. His phone number is (602) 315-4732.

Mike McCain builds the occasional tow mixer. You can call him at the number listed in our "Resources" section on page 96. He is in the process of building a tow mixer for me for $350. I would imagine if he got a lot of calls, he would have to raise his price. Considering how much production a tow mixer is capable of, $350 sounds like a very reasonable price to me. Incidentally, Mike is now experimenting with using plastic water tanks that he gets in Mexico instead of the steel stock tanks. The stock tanks, he has found, tend to crack after a year or so of being towed around.

This just goes to show that papercrete experimenters are learning as we go. We try something, and if it doesn't work, we try something else. It's the most exciting way to live—constantly pushing the envelope. To keep up with this continual learning process, we will be putting out *Papercrete Journal*—an ongoing update of state-of-the-art papercrete and paper adobe information. New information is coming in all the time, and we intend to keep up with it.

Papercrete and paper adobe are such obvious and useful concepts that it's only a matter of time until they receive the recognition they deserve. Rather than throwing "waste" paper and cardboard into landfills, we can turn it into a valuable building material. It's a golden opportunity for this country to start managing its solid waste "problem" with a little common sense.

Reference Guide

This book is mostly articles from **Earth Quarterly**. In these articles, we occasionally refer back to articles in previous issues. Since the page numbers in this book are different from the page numbers in the magazine, we are printing this reference guide to make it easier to find the material we're referring to.

PAGE NUMBER IN THIS BOOK	REFERENCE TO EARTH QUARTERLY	GO TO THIS PAGE IN THIS BOOK
36	Issue #1, page 4	9
36	#1, p. 7	12
41	#1, p. 3	8
55	#1, p. 13	18
56	#2, p. 20	40
61	#3, p. 14	54
64	#1, p. 13	18
64	#1, p. 14	19
65	#3, p. 16	56

RESOURCES
(Updated March 2002)

• Our 2-hour video, **Building with Papercrete and Paper Adobe,** is available for $39 postpaid from Papercrete News, Box 23, Radium Springs, NM 88054). Please make check out to Gordon Solberg.

• There is now a papercrete egroup at the following address: <http://groups.yahoo.com/group/papercretenews/>. I cofounded this group in March 2000. There are now 175 members and over 2400 messages posted in the archives.

• Our website, <www.zianet.com/papercrete> has a lot of the photos from this book in full color.

• <www.padobe.com> has a lot of good info.

• My article in the May 2000 **Mother Earth News** is a basic overview that will be of interest to papercrete aficionados. I couldn't find any info on their website about ordering back issues. Their web address is <www.motherearthnews.com>.

• My article in the Nov/Dec 2000 issue of **BackHome** is a slightly different slant from my MEN article. This issue can be purchased online for $3.75 from <www.backhomemagazine.com>.

• Tim Pye and Cathryn Swann have a site about the papercrete house they built in Cornville, AZ: <www.moonsinger.com/casawizardmoon.htm>.

• Kelly Hart's site, <www.greenhomebuilder.com>, has a lot of information about papercrete.

A Simple Sawdust/Cordwood Shelter

Sean Sands

INTRODUCTION

This article gives information about how to construct a circular 214 square foot shelter, including a six foot entrance passage, for a cost, excluding labour, of about US$250. This cost assumes that materials such as stone, sand, and waste lumber products (such as sawdust and cordwood) are freely available on site (otherwise, these costs and transportation costs will need to be factored in). The structure can be built by one person within two weeks, and will provide suitable accommodation for two people.

A sketch is available. Please send me a SASE for a copy or for additional information: Sean Sands, Box 4, Grand Forks, BC, Canada, V0H 1H0; or email: flotsam@jetstream.net.

STEPS IN CONSTRUCTION

1. Choose a site and clear the ground of organic materials. There is no need to level the site.

2. Establish the internal (16 foot diameter) and external (20 foot diameter) dimensions of the structure, using a central pivot and stretching a cord to describe one circle with a radius of 10 feet, and another with a radius of 8 feet.

3. Lay down an initial ring of mortar between the boundaries of these circles to form a pad for the structure. Clay and straw may be used as mortar.

4. Lay a first tier of 18" cordwood, with the inside edges touching the internal boundaries of the structure where marked upon the pad.

5. Complete each tier of the structure, using cordwood embedded in mortar, leaving openings for the door, windows, skylight, air tube, and smokestack. The mortar consists of a mixture of 1 part of cement to 3 parts of sand, placed in a wheelbarrow and thoroughly mixed with a hoe. Twelve parts of sawdust are added and mixed in until the composition is a homogeneous grey. Water is then added until the mixture is saturated, but without excessive water. Each tier is self-supporting and self-locking, since any tendency to collapse is met with its own resistance. Forms are unnecessary, since each tier of cordwood is cantilevered inwardly, with most of each tier resting on the tier beneath it, eventually providing a dome-shaped structure. The force of gravity assists this process and adds strength to the structure. The ends of the cordwood in each tier are pointed to provide a final finish for the inner surface areas of the structure, thus saving any need for time-consuming and frustrating plastering of surfaces.

6. For the outside of the structure, the cordwood is sealed with a thick coat of plaster to add strength and insulation. The mortar for this is composed of sawdust and cement, or of paper and cement. Further waterproofing, initially using clear plastic sheets, later replaced by a finishing sealer, reduces maintenance costs to almost nil.

7. The spiral door passage is six feet long and provides an airlock, divided by two sets of curtains.

8. Place and seal the window and door units. These, including frames and glass, may be discarded units from construction sites, and may be placed, as is, into their openings, and then sealed into the surrounding walls with mortar.

9. Excavate under the dome to a 3 foot depth, depositing the material outside and surrounding the structure to form an artificial hill (to provide drainage).

10. Dig a fire pit to provide light, heat, and a base for a small cooking stove (or use a discarded truck wheel hub to contain a cooking fire). Above these, suspend from the roof a smoke-cone and -stack, with the stack extending through the roof aperture. Using hazelnut or similar flexible wooden stems, weave a cone to surround the smoke-stack at the roof aperture. This is a removable cover (when this is removed, during favourable weather, additional light enters the structure).

11. Place and seal an earth-sheltered, screened air-tube in the opening already prepared for it.

12. Provide two five-gallon buckets for toilet and kitchen waste disposal. Immediately after using these, their contents should be sealed with a thin layer of sawdust until they can be removed to become composting materials.

13. If desired, long poles may be projected over the dome's windows and door passageway, to form rain and sun shields.

MATERIALS USED

- Cordwood, freely available from forests, cut into 18" lengths to give final 2' walls.
- Sawdust, about 3000 gallons, available from local sawmills, gratis, except for transportation costs.
- Sand, about 6 tons, freely available on site.
- Cement, about two tons.

• Windows, skylight, doors, cook-stove, smoke-cone and -stack, air-tube, curtains, buckets, tools: freely available from dump sites or at nominal cost at thrift stores.

ADVANTAGES

• A basic tent or teepee of this size costs as much, is not as permanent, and is not as resistant to fire, wind, and temperature fluctuations.

View looking in the front door, showing overhanging log entryway.

• Construction is simple, low cost, requires only hand tools such as a hoe, bow-saw, and wheelbarrow (not even a truck is needed) and indigenous materials, and does not demand any heavy lifting, or footings, or forms. It can be done by anyone with limited strength and with no building experience.

• The structure's circular, domed shape, lightweight construction materials, and 24" walls provide intrinsic tensile integrity and strength, widely distributed (as compared to conventional cordwood structures having vertical walls).

• It requires cordwood that may be obtained, gratis, from forest windfalls, deadwood, and branches that are not commercially valuable and that would normally be burned in slash-piles (as compared to commercially available cordwood that must be dried for up to two years to reduce shrinking and cracking).

• There is no lead-time requirement, a most significant consideration in the event of a natural disaster requiring that alternative shelter be found.

• Excavating is done after the dome has been completed and is thus not hampered by inclement weather.

• The structure is highly insulating. Being partially underground, the structure is below the frost line, is warmer in winter and cooler in summer than conventional structures. Less

fuel is therefore needed for heating or cooling. The composition of sand, sawdust, and cement retains the ambient temperature and so is resistant to temperature changes, thus providing a flywheel effect between night and day temperatures.

• Repair and maintenance jobs are easily and cheaply done.

• The earth at my location is about 80% rock, gravel, and sand, which provides good drainage.

• The structure is ecologically supportive.

ADDITIONAL NOTES

Basically, what I'm trying to redress is the imbalance that is occurring in the industrialized world where the individual or family work themselves to death to be able to afford a shelter that goes way beyond need and requires a fortune to maintain, heat and cool—while at the same time polluting the environment, and exploiting the labour and resources of other people.

So—the principles I'm looking for in shelter and the maintenance of shelters are:

Interior view showing how cordwood ends make an attractive wall.

1. Smaller (more need related) shelters.
2. Indigenous materials.
3. Simplicity.
4. Stability with advent of markedly changing climates (swings of temperature), wind, fire, etc.
5. Ecological implications.
6. Low cost.

7. Availability—low-tech, common materials easily handled by 1 or 2 people.

8. Flexibility/mobility—skills of empowerment. Creation of one's shelter imbues one with confidence that if a location becomes uninhabitable by virtue of cost, pollution, violence, Earth changes, etc., one can move out to an area more conducive to health and happiness.

9. Technology (appropriate)—tending as much as possible to hand tools, with the energy labour intensive as much as possible.

10. Clean, available, low cost, natural, indigenous, unprocessed methods of heating and cooling (sun, geothermal or earth, local dead wood).

11. High energy efficiency of dwellings—insulation where needed, and thermal mass where needed.

12. Safety—where the process of building and final structure are inducive to health.

13. Rapid construction to avoid rent, mortgage, commuting, and weather deterioration.

With these characteristics in mind, the two problems I have with fibrous cement are (1) machinery—e.g., cost, technical expertise required, fossil fuels, pollution, mechanical breakdown, danger, and health considerations; and (2) cement—energy requirement, pollution with CO_2, and any toxicity of house.

Last summer's sawdust/cordwood dome project comes closer to my ideal in that the technology is simpler (wheelbarrow, hoe,

Ladder extending up into skylight area.

bow saw), cheaper, can be used for other purposes, is non-polluting, more available, safer, and healthier.

The cement was used because I didn't have a truck or locally available clay. With clay and chopped straw or cow manure, I suspect I could have built the structure and then surface bonded and/or waterproofed it with greenhouse plaster initially to secure the structure against moisture.

For this structure I dig down only one foot because I was under trees and would have disturbed the roots if I had gone deeper.

However, ideally constructing the dome first and moving under it to excavate 3-4 feet down with a ledge or bench at the perimeter would allow one to get in quickly out of the weather. You could live inside, and would have a protected microclimate to work in when ordinarily rain, snow, heat, or wind would seriously curtail construction.

The entry would be a snail-like wraparound gently sloping ramp (wheelchair accessible) which would allow a wheelbarrow to easily remove excavated material. A door or curtain at grade and one on entry would provide an air lock.

The excavated material would be placed as a berm around the

Two views of the completed dome.

northern aspect of the building, for further earth sheltering, energy efficiency, protection from high winds, fire, etc.

Again, the advantages of the dome: 15-25% greater floor area for the same perimeter of wall than a square or rectangle. Intrinsic strength. There will be no dead air spaces when you use a central heater for equal distribution of heat.

Laying in an air tube that wraps around the building before berming it with material from excavation allows for earth-tempered fresh air in the building (cool in summer, warm in winter rather than harsh drafts).

Dead cordwood is ideal in this area (non-commercially viable), light, easy to handle, insulating.

The internal surface area is less than the exterior surface area, so the cordwood on the inside is nearly touching. Each concentric circle creates a self-locking ring of wood (any tendency to fall in on itself opposes itself) so the structure can be built simply with a string to define the radius—thus, no forms are necessary, and no prior knowledge—because of the simplicity of merely touching the 8-foot string to the cordwood end. This is all the template one needs.

If wood weren't available, clay paper blocks or papercrete blocks could be used.

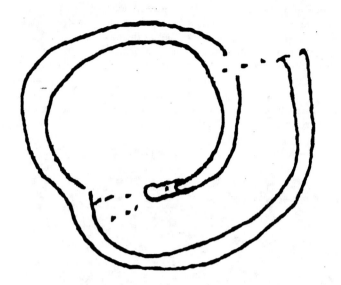

Spiral entryway to dome

The advantage of having cordwood or preformed blocks is that the lightness and structural stability allows one to proceed rapidly in putting the dome up without having to wait for the curing. Give a light structure with high insulation qualities.

The interior surface of the building (which overhead is difficult to plaster) is already finished with the cordwood ends.

It is easy to plaster over the outside of the entire structure with gravity assisting. The plaster seals any potential cracks in the structure resulting from cordwood shrinkage. (The real limitation of traditional cordwood structures is the lengthy curing time (up to 1-2 years) because on a vertical wall plastering cracks is so tedious and time-consuming.)

A dome-like skylight can be constructed as a basket with hazelnut (or any supple branches) lashed together with a short piece of insulated pipe though the centre. This would be a sleeve to run a small piece of stovepipe through. The skylight dome is enveloped in greenhouse plaster to give the skylight a source of light with the dome easily shedding any snow or rain.

Every aspect of this cordwood dome can be done by one person as all units involved are easily lifted and require no technical ability.

A cone could be suspended from the stove stack to allow a small open fire for light and heat. You could use a truck wheel casing or rocks for the firepit, or use a small wood cookstove or an orno (adobe dome baking oven).

Composting toilet system using sawdust layering of human waste in 5-gallon plastic buckets with toilet seat has been used very satisfactorily for 13 years in British Columbia and in New Mexico.

In our case, the windows, curtains, buckets, stove, stovepipe, and air tube were scrounged from the local landfill.

The windows were simply mortared into place using standard mortar mix or adobe and straw, or papercrete, or cow manure.

A friend recently came up with a simple way to shred paper: Presoak paper and place in cement mixer with water and a dozen orange-sized ball bearings. Tumble and then screen out the metal balls. The paper pulp or fiber could then be mixed with adobe or cement-stabilized adobe to give a light insulating block with tensile strength.

PAPERCRETE PERSPECTIVES (Continued from page 42)
was built, it would be covered with a hard, waterproof stucco containing cement and whatever waterproofing agents were available. The materials cost for such a structure would be next to nothing, and it would retain the advantages of light weight, great strength, and high insulating value.

THE ULTIMATE PAPER BUNGALOW

No matter how cheaply you could build a dome, most Americans would prefer a home that conforms to a more middle-class ideal. It needs to look and perform like a "real" house. Such a house would need to have a concrete foundation, and windows to provide light, ventilation, and a view. Plumbing and wiring would be expected. But of all these luxuries, only the windows would add significantly to the cost, and it is possible to buy used windows very cheaply. The **Earth Quarterly** office, illustrated elsewhere in this issue, is a good example of how a low-cost paper building can have a "conventional" appearance.

CONCLUSION

There is no doubt that papercrete is an amazing building material with enormous potential. There are many dozens of people who are already experimenting with it, and this number will soon grow to the hundreds, and thousands.

An accomplished scrounge hound could build a modest but very decent home out of papercrete for $1000 or less. In an era when more and more people are locked out of the housing market by excessive prices and mortgage rates, this is an astounding and—dare I say it—revolutionary idea.

This country wastes a criminal amount of resources. Creating a use for all the countless tons of waste paper that never even make it into the recycle bins would be a major step in the right direction. It would be highly desirable if we could actually start redeeming ourselves (as opposed to merely talking about it).

Papercrete is unique in that it can be manufactured not only by the individual inventor with a home-made mixer, but by huge factories turning out thousands of blocks a day. In fact, it won't be until papercrete production is industrialized that papercrete will reach its full potential. A very small percentage of the population will actually build their own papercrete mixers so that they can manufacture their own paper blocks. Substantially more people would be willing to buy a mixer so that they could make blocks. But it won't be until papercrete blocks are as common as cinderblocks, and can be purchased at any lumberyard, that the "papercrete movement" will have the mainstream acceptance it deserves. And in order to have mainstream acceptance, papercrete would need to be accepted by the building code authorities—and it will take years to jump through all the necessary hoops.

Till then, we—the grassroots sustainability pioneers—are on our own (which is a good thing, actually). It's discouraging not to have any meaningful leadership from the top, but at least we are free to do whatever we feel we can get away with (and we're usually pretty successful at this). Papercrete today is where straw bale was in 1985. Astounding developments are in store. Future issues of **Earth Quarterly** will have lots of new papercrete information—innovative building projects, new mixer designs, personal experiences and feedback. Till next issue, always remember:

**DON'T WORRY,
MIX SLURRY!**

LETTERS

I received issues #1 & 2 of **Earth Quarterly** & was very impressed. I'm 41 & been in home building & remodeling most all my life. I hope to be leaving Ohio fairly soon & was gona move back out west somewhere. I went to school in Deming & also lived in Las Cruces & because I'm so interested in this "fibrous cement" I've decided to move back to that area. I look forward to meeting & working with you & others to improve & work with this product. Keep up the good work & open mind!

Scott Childress
Orient, OH

Just borrowed 1st issue of **Earth Quarterly**—awesome! I've seen one dome built from papercrete. We are building a mixer and going to really promote this idea here.

Also, many large companies—especially news organizations—have bins & bins of shredded paper cut back—glad to have someone haul it away!

Hawk
Arivaca, AZ

I am truly impressed with your magazine.

Paula Porter
Springfield, TN

Here in the Hudson Valley we are exploring many ways to make our lifestyle more sustainable. For several years we have been working on sustainable agriculture (sponsoring conferences, evens, a buy local campaign, etc.) Currently we are focusing on sustainable building practices. Amongst other initiatives, one of our local contractors, John Dawson, has been experimenting with a fiber-based construction block. John had been planning to research what's already been done in this area, but he's been very busy.

Then, about a month ago, our friend William Henry brought in an issue of **Earth Quarterly** to our "Voluntary Simplicity" study group. Lo and behold, here was a ready source of information. Although John was unaware of the work on papercrete and fibrous cement, I'm sure he will benefit greatly from contacting Eric Patterson, Mike McCain, Kelly Hart and others.

I also noticed the Hart's video ad on the back page of the issue ("A Sampler of Alternative Homes: Approaching Sustainable Architecture") and have since purchased three copies—one to keep, one to lend (there's been lots of interest) and one to send to Scotland where it is being copied into PAL to send to two separate communities in Russia that are working on sustainable building projects. It's very well done and I highly recommend it to anyone interested in this subject.

John Dawson's situation of thinking he was inventing fiber blocks, but not realizing that a good deal of work has already been done, is reminiscent of the start of our local sustainability group. About five years ago a dozen or so concerned citizens got together to explore ways of linking environmental protection with economic well-being and social justice. We earnestly thought that we had invented the concept of sustainability! Little did we know that for over 20 years people have been working on this all over the world. Thanks to the Internet, we are widely networked and doing our small part in the bigger picture of creating (and rediscovering) more sustainable ways of living on this beautiful planet.

Thanks for being there.

Manna Jo Greene
Hudson Valley Sustainable
Communities Network
Cottekill, NY

Your **Earth Quarterly** is making waves in Tucson. EQ seems to be getting lots of attention, are you feeling it?

Linda Drew
Tucson, AZ

So that's what that is!

Here's how I make papercrete stucco for my tire house: I use a shortened edger blade on a 1/2 inch drill. The paper is shredded first in a leaf wacker. I dump a couple of pounds (?) or so of the shredded paper into a 55-gallon barrel that's been cut in half, add about five gallons of water, add three shovel fulls of portland cement, two of sand, a couple tablespoons of air entrainment, and mix for five or ten minutes with the drill/edger blade. Makes a good stucco mix. I realize I use quite a bit of portland, but the stucco is just an inch thick and I need the strength. Also, I feel it makes the mix more fire retardant.

David Stebbins
Canyon, TX

Your letter reminds me—there's a company that makes a gizmo called the "Mix-It" which they say will mix anything from paint to concrete. Its main limitation is its small size—5 gallons. Try their web site: www.mixitinc.com, or write to them at Mix-It, 7800 E. 12th St., Kansas City, MO 64126.

Can you send me a copy of **Earth Quarterly** No. 1? I got your e-mail address from a friend of mine in New Mexico. He said that the physical address on the back cover was worn off but he was able to get the e-mail address.

Olen Northern
Anchorage, AK

Yes, our first issue got used a lot!

What a wonderful issue. Fascinating. The article on our visit is quite well done and I am getting a lot of favorable comments. I like the way you presented my

Many of the letters from Earth Quarterly are about papercrete. Even the ones that aren't about papercrete are interesting to read.

thought and feel it is quite complete except that I wish we had talked about the need for an effective process of forgiveness. In every relationship or community there are difficulties and it is corrosive to hang on to them or tally them. Here we have feuds that last a lifetime because there is no effective mechanism for giving each other a fresh start. We cannot afford smoldering hostility when we need so desperately to work together for the benefit of all.

Thanks for all your work.

Barbara Kerr
Taylor, AZ

I just received the 3rd edition of your publication and must say I am thoroughly impressed. Keep up the good work.

Joseph Birkett, Editor
The Connection
Arivaca, AZ

The Connection is an excellent monthly newspaper serving rural south-central Arizona. For a sample copy, send $2 to them at P.O. Box 338-EQ, Arivaca, AZ 85601.

My heart leaped when I received your special "Paper House" issue of **Earth Quarterly**. I've worked for years trying to devise a way to make homes from recycled materials that would be functional &

beautiful. You definitely filled in some blanks for me & I am thankful to you. Best wishes as you continue to build these wonderful houses.

Kristi Cadwell
Richland, WA

EQ #3 is fantastic! I read it pretty much in one sitting. I loved the interview with Barbara Kerr...she's awesome and so matter-of-fact. You can tell she's a woman that has walked the road, not just talked it...something we all want to really strive to do. We'd love to visit her place.

Also, the article by Michael Smith was great... so healing and yearning to see collaboration rather than competition take place. I thought he really put natural building into proper perspective by challenging all of us to be big enough to see the beauty in our differentness rather than being threatened by it. WOW! This is something we can all learn from, isn't it?

I think the magazine is wonderful because this message comes through in many places. Are we really willing to embrace our differentness, yet be able to reach out to each other in friendship and understanding? I think this came out in the interview with John Jeavons, in his discussions on community. John's message

is a much needed one and it really calls us all forth to create a better future.

The Lauratorial was beautiful! I loved the line, "If you seek a pleasant community, look about you!" I've been pondering that a lot this week and last. We so often look everywhere but right in front of us! Who are the ones that are community to us? Who are the ones that we have bonded with and grown to love despite the trials and tribulations and "snits"? Who are the ones that bring us joy and life and fresh air and support? It doesn't mean we are all the same, does it? It doesn't mean that we will see everything the same way or approach things the same, yet we love each other in spite of it...because of it!

I sure am learning this: that differentness may be uncomfortable and unnerving; it may shake a lot of my walls that I can so easily erect to protect myself from the fears and vulnerabilities I have deep within, but if I am really to embrace community and learn to love and be a whole person, and be shaped by the beauty of other people around me, then I have to tear down the walls, open myself up to their uniqueness, and receive their gift of differentness, and, yes, even the things about the other person that may make me squirm at times.

AN INNOVATIVE "SEMI-SUSTAINABLE" ROOF DESIGN

When Greg Jay and I were preparing for our 1999 papercrete workshop, we decided to make part of the papercrete office roof as sustainable as we could, using native materials where possible. We decided to use a barrel vault design because it is simple and strong. Our first choice was to use willow poles for the framework, but since the workshop was less than a week away, we decided to use rebar instead. We simply didn't have time to cut and trim the willow poles in that amount of time, in addition to all our other tasks.

This photo shows the rebar framework in place. The ribs, made of 3/8" rebar, are spaced 20" apart. The rebar is too thin—it supports the

roof, but just barely. The only reason it works is because the span is only 6 feet. Half inch rebar would have been better. For the back wall, we drove 3-foot-long rebar spikes into the papercrete, and welded the ribs to the spikes. For the front wall, use screwed lag screws into the wood and welded the ribs to the lag screws.

Then we lashed cane perpendicular to the ribs. We used baling wire, weaving the cane to the rebar. Cane, a relative to bamboo, is used as an ornamental here in southern New Mexico, and I have a lot of it growing on my property. Although it isn't as strong as bamboo, cane is plenty strong enough for this application.

In this photo, notice the horizontal reinforcing

(Continued on p. 112)

It isn't always easy to do, but hopefully, as we learn to do this, we realize that in the process, something has happened, and a semblance of commUNITY has been developed...maybe that's it: COMing together in UNITY. Unity doesn't mean sameness, robots, or automatons that all mimic each other. It means coming together with all that we have, good and bad, and offering ourselves for the good of others, to build something that we as a group benefit from, and that we all can offer to others outside our little circles.

Amber Vallotton
Las Cruces, NM

Earth Quarterly contains useful, practical information; meeting the needs of the can-do, low tech craftsperson. Keep up the good work.

Allan Leake
Silver City, NM

"Radium Springs" sounds a bit ominous. Is it?

Bob Wallace
Orocovis, PR

The town of Radium Springs got its name from the Radium Hot Springs Resort, which was started in the 20s. Back then, radium was thought to have healing properties, so the resort promoters used "Radium" in the name for the hype value. The water from the hot springs does contain trace amounts of radium, but no more than is usually found in geothermal water. Even so, people from Radium Springs are rumored to have that "special glow."

Finding **Earth Quarterly** has been a happy experience. Wish you printed more often.

Virginia Stepp
Tujunga, CA

Maybe we'll change our name to **Earth Wheneverly** *and come out whenever we feel like it, which would probably be every day or two.*

I stumbled onto your web site via Simple Living Net. I "surf" a lot, and check out lots of sites; yours really grabbed me and now I want a subscription to the printed magazine. Your editorials are so very well written and express such hopeful, positive beliefs. And I <u>have</u> to find out what papercrete is all about!

I am an apartment dweller working toward owning a home, and a warrior by trade (I'm in the military.) I left my homesteading project 14 years ago when I realized I lacked resources and commitment to the sheer work of it (we bit off more than we could chew). I since joined the Navy and have spent the last 10 years living on islands and ships, but I've never lost my passion for gardening, small animal husbandry, and solar technologies, etc. True, as a willing employee of the great war-mongering, military-industrial complex, I am not in most people's eyes a good "back-to-the-earth" candidate. The Navy only recycles because it is mandated to, for instance, and there is a strong corporate aversion to environmentalists (think Greenpeace vs. Navy). Both my spirituality and my commitment to living sustainably make me an anomaly among my peers, but I consider it a personal challenge to "bridge the gap" between the opposing viewpoints and spread the good word whenever I can.

I am learning so much from people like you! Your magazine is helping to build the culture of the future by connecting so many people to these ideas. Just a few more years of service and I'll be able to get back to my gardens and my orchards and my goats. Thank God people like you are still out there, still teaching.

Kay Gschwind
La Mesa, CA

I'm planning to build a timber-fibrous concrete house. In spite of its cheapness, the qualities of f.c. are outstanding. And the component materials are mostly environmentally correct to boot. Thanks a lot.

Clarence Ching
Kamuela, HI

Thanks for a real nice magazine. May your success continue and growth allow you to become a major competitor in alternative and modern living. Thank you and keep up the dreams—for some, they will become reality—others hope.

Clyde W. Seymour
Bellefonte, PA

The Quarterly—we don't see how the two of you put out such a publication! It is wonderfully interesting & practical.

Mary Brown
Las Cruces, NM

It must be all the raw carrot juice we drink!

Do you know if anyone has experimented with using gypsum (plaster of paris) instead of cement in papercrete? There is a man doing this with earth and pumping this directly into forms for walls for houses. If you're interested, here is the site address: <www.castearth.com>.

Paul Sarnstrom
hoh@rmi.net

Let me begin by telling you how much I enjoyed this latest issue. You both voiced many sentiments I share about community and living a life well loved. John Jeavons' interview really hit home for me too. And I'd love to meet Barbara Kerr. I'd like to meet you guys some day too.

On the subject of dirt bags, prices are at an all-time low for large amounts: 4 to 5 cents apiece for several thousand. Plus whatever shipping is to your area. Call Cady Industries (1-800-243-2451) and ask for Lisa Young. Tell her Kaki in Moab sent you. I've filled her in on our exploits. She has also got terrific deals on untreated burlap bags. Burlap costs more to ship, but for slow builders in a dry climate they will endure the sun for a year or two. Woven poly bags have a 2-5 month window before disintegrating to the UVs.

I would like to introduce the process of earth bag construction with some pages from our manual. We are beginning to get calls for more info and construction supervision. We're just barely able to keep up. Voluntary simplicity is indeed a challenge for our "swept up by the excitement of all the possibilities of life" moments. Ah yes, I know you know too well. **Earth Quarterly** is your vehicle for exploratory travel and discovery, too. Love sharing with you.

Kaki Hunter
Moab, UT

In watching some of the straw bale videos, reading the books, etc. I noticed that many of you are from the same area of NM. Is there a reason or draw to this place?

Bob Bryant
Renton, WA

I'll never tell! Seriously, it's the combination of a magical spirit of the land with a relatively benign winter climate.

We love EQ and wish you every blessing. Only, don't become so "successful" that you are forced to sell out. Those of us (the majority) in the real world need accurate, useful information at affordable rates.

Meg Keoppen
Arivaca, AZ

Thanks for your excellent advice!

I loved issue #3! Was especially moved by Linda Drew's "The Splitting of the Ways," and the Lauratorial. Thanks for **Earth Quarterly**.

Alice Swanson
Old Joe, AR

After that lovely issue of the magazine arrived, I meant to email and say how much

103

I loved it, but time slipped away. I found Barbara Kerr especially inspiring. Watch out, you guys... your magazine could grow big time!

Rosana Hart
Crestone, CO

It's a joy to see EQ-3 getting better and better! Nice variety of things to read and ponder—

I wonder if papercrete floats? Has anyone tried making a hull out of it and sealed it for launching? There are ferro-cement boats out there that are strong and still sailing. Just a thought, albeit a weird one!

Thanks so much again for a great issue!

Marcus Bachino
Williams, OR

Unsealed papercrete absorbs water like a sponge. If you thoroughly sealed a papercrete boat with silicone, it should float. I'm not sure if I would trust the sealer to keep the boat from eventually sinking, however.

Here's some feedback on issue #3: I really like the editorials, the interviews, and the hands-on stuff. The reviews are great, with a good selection. I really liked the balance of different sorts of information, from the personal to the technical. It makes EQ an interesting read. Overall, this is great, great work. I am very impressed.

Michael Smith
Sebastopol, CA

Please extend our subscription to **Earth Quarterly**. I haven't a clue when it expires, but don't want to take a chance on missing even one issue of your great little publication. Sittin' here waitin' for the next issue already!

Gayle and George O'Dell
Hesperia, CA

I DEEPLY, DEEPLY loved the interview with Barbara Kerr. Probably what I'm really saying is: I DEEPLY, DEEPLY love Barbara Kerr! Her wisdom, compassion, sensibility, stamina, attitude, etc. My very favorite part was the "Singing and Dancing" section.

I've been in the process of creating an out-of-sight dancing area in the "loft" (attic) but now I believe I'll bring my tap shoes down to the kitchen!

I was about to write that at 53 years of age & 200 pounds of weight, I'm no nymph. But I decided to look up nymph: *"One of the minor divinities of nature that are represented as beautiful maidens dwelling in the mountains, forests, meadows and waters."*

I LIKE THAT! I LIKE THAT <u>A</u> <u>LOT</u>!! Maybe I really AM a 53-year-old, 200-pound NYMPH after all. Thank you, Barbara! (And Laura.)

Iona
Libertytown, MD

I ran into a guy in a cafe in Study Butte, TX this weekend who talked about papercrete. I did an aol search and you came up #1. And guess what? That guy, Mark Spurlock, came up in your site's letters section!

Bob Brewer
Carrollton, TX
Yes, it's a small papercrete world!

I really enjoyed your article on Barbara Kerr. I met her several years ago in Taylor, AZ and I'm so happy to know she is continuing her sustainable living. Please print more articles of this nature.

Mrs. Carol Swartz
Arivaca, AZ

Congratulations on the last issue. Awesome! Am still reading and rereading it. So much information. How can you top it?

Pam Smith
Las Cruces, NM
That's an excellent question!

Hope your next issue is soon. We really enjoy them.

Eve Jameson
Kingman, AZ

Dear fellow papercreters,

I would like to share my mixing experiences with anyone who might have an interest. I have a heavy duty mortar mixer which I stuffed with pre-soaked, shredded paper. I let the mixer churn it for about 5 minutes, adding water as needed, and it turned to a slurry that looked like oatmeal. I poured this into a big washtub and then shoveled it back into the mixer along with the usual mix of sand and cement and then into some adobe forms. When I get enough blocks I plan to build a small toolhouse with a domed roof (which may take some trial and error to accomplish).

The shredded paper came from our local city hall and high school (they were glad to get rid of it). I also have access to lots of junk mail from the local recycle yard and they let me use their paper shredder.

Just thought I would pass this on.

Tom "slurry" Curry
Alpine, TX
curry@brooksdata.net

"ORGANIC REBAR"

These are roof panels (see p. 145). The form is made of 2x6" lumber, and is 3 feet wide and 8 feet long. When this photo was taken, the form was filled halfway with slurry, and two pieces of cane were laid side-by-side for each roof panel, to serve as "organic rebar." Small saplings would also serve this purpose well.

The forms were then filled to the top, and after about an hour the slurry was cut in the middle, giving us 6 panels, 1 foot wide and 4 feet long. After shrinkage, the panels were about 4" thick.

ANOTHER USE FOR PAPER PULP

When we built our fidobe guest house, we used a cinderblock stem wall to raise the fidobe 8" off the ground. We decided to insulate the cinderblocks with paper pulp. We just filled our mixer with paper and water, pulped it together, and poured it into the blocks. Since there was no need for strength, we didn't need to add cement to the slurry. The slurry shrank considerably, and we ended up topping off the blocks two additional times.

Special Papercrete Issue

Earth Quarterly

No. 5   **$5.00**

Papercrete in Wisconsin

Paul Reavis' 14x16-foot cordwood/papercrete barn addition.

When Laura went to the Midwest Renewable Energy Fair in Wisconsin this past June, she met EQ subscriber Paul Reavis, of Brodhead, WI, who told her about his papercrete building projects. Ever on the alert for article opportunities, Laura asked Paul if he would e-mail us the details. He graciously did so, as well as sending us some photographs. I have assembled his e-mails and photographs into the following article. Direct quotes from his e-mails are in italics.

At the Midwest Renewable Energy Fair, Laura was asked one question most frequently: "What about building with papercrete in a humid climate?" We hope that this article provides some inspiration for humid climate papercreters.

—GS

Paul first learned about papercrete in 1986, when he inherited an extensive collection of *Popular Mechanics, Mechanix Illustrated,* and *Popular Science* magazines, that dated from the 50s up to 1979. He read through all those magazines and saved the articles he was interested in, and accumulated a file cabinet full of interesting articles. Two of these articles were about paper construction. One of the articles was written way back in 1954, and the other appeared in the November, 1973 issue of *Popular Mechanics.*

Paul became interested in the possibility of using paper as a substitute for sawdust in log end (cordwood) construction. Further, he was interested in finding a way to recycle waste paper. *I used to discuss inventions a lot of the time with the guy who worked next to me back then. I used to talk about how to find a way to recycle all the paper that they threw out at work.*

Paul started working with papercrete in 1988 (which makes him one of the paleolithic pioneers of modern papercreting), when he built a cordwood addition onto his barn.

His method of making papercrete was very simple—he tore newspapers into 1" strips and threw them into an old water tank to soak... for at least a day, sometimes longer. He just kept adding strips as time went by, so the paper at the bottom of the tank tended to slurry, while the newer paper at the top remained intact. He pulled the soaked paper out of the tank by hand and threw it into a wheelbarrow which already contained premixed mortar (he guesses that this was 3 parts sand to 1 part cement). He estimates that his ratio was 40% mortar (which he mixed in the wheelbarrow before adding the paper) and 60% paper (by volume). Then he mixed the paper and mortar together with a hoe. *I never used a formula, just added cement and sand till it was sticking together and looking right. I imagine the cement content was pretty high compared to what is now used.*

I used papercrete for the mortar between cordwood on an addition to my horse barn in 1988. At the time I was just

Another view of the cordwood/papercrete barn addition.

This is a closeup of the barn. Gaps are visible from the pine log end shrinkage.

experimenting with a way to use paper and didn't know anything about anybody else doing it. I had read one of Rob Roy's books on how to build Log End houses. Since I had an abundance of pine logs and needed a hay storage area, I added a 14x16-foot addition. I made it in sections, 4x6 feet each section, timberframing with 4x6" posts. I used short cordwood—about 8" long—since it was just for a barn.

Paul is pleased with how well the papercrete has stood up in his relatively extreme Wisconsin climate. They get an average of 32" of rain a year, and 30" of snow. There is snow on the ground an average of 85 days a year, and temperatures reach -30° almost every winter. He says that the papercrete is standing up better than the wood. *In 11 years, the only shrinkage is at the top, a gap of about 1/4-1/2". Some of the log ends will move if you push on them. I*

suspect that the gap at the top is due to settling, and the logs' moving is due to wood shrinkage more than paper shrinkage. I've never noticed a problem with water soaking into the papercrete, probably due to the high cement content.

People are always asking EQ about bug problems with papercrete, especially termites. Paul says he's never had any trouble with termites.

Paul has recently built a tow mixer, and has plans for several more projects. *I plan on making a growing dome first and then a garage with papercrete as soon as I get going on actual block construction. As of yet I don't know what kind of problems I will run into with codes on the garage. I plan on timberframing and infilling with the papercrete as I tore down an old barn a few years ago and have lots of beams.*

This mold, which utilizes a hydraulic log splitter to squeeze excess water out of the slurry, was built in an attempt to speed up the drying process. The log splitter provides 20 tons of pressure. (For a similar concept, see the article on Travis Coffey in Earth Quarterly #2.) As this is a recently finished project, Paul has made only a couple of blocks with it. The opening at the top needs to be made larger, so that the slurry can be poured into the mold more quickly. The finished blocks will be approximately 6x8x12". The mold was made with 1/2" steel with a 3/4" plunger.

This solar kiln/dryer is another attempt to hurry the drying process, due to the high humidity in the Midwest. Without a dryer, blocks take at least six weeks to dry in this climate. The 9x9-foot dryer consists of a frame made of 2x4s, covered with double clear plastic on the top and east/west sides. There is a single layer on the south. The north wall is black plastic, for maximum heat absorption. There is a 1 foot opening at the bottom of the east and west sides for air flow.

He has encountered a situation that many people can relate to: *I called the township this week to see about building permits, and found out that they hired a new building inspector who is by the book all the way. I may have a lot of trouble with this one. I knew the old one, and he had a lot of common sense and would try to work with a person. I am thinking now of building a gazebo first, just as an experiment, since I shouldn't need a permit for that. Maybe that will help with the new inspector. If not, I'm looking for land in Missouri and Arkansas again, where I know there aren't any codes.*

How does it feel, being for years the only papercrete builder in the Upper Midwest? *There is not a lot of encouragement from people around here. If I talk about papercrete, they just kind of look at me funny, like "What are you talking about?" They are very helpful about giving me paper, though. Which is why I have to get my mixer going as fast as possible.*

People wanting to contact Paul Reavis can e-mail him at <grundune@brodnet.com>.

is to drain the water, if you need to move the barrel or if the water goes bad. *Drill another hole in the bottom half, 2" from the top, for the hose and electrical cord for the water pump. Put the water pump in and fill with water. The bottom section is done.*

To make the top half, drill as many 3/8" drainage holes as you can. Cut 2 slots for handles, so that you can lift the top half off and empty the slurry. I routed a semi-circle into the board (I used a 1" closet shelf) to fit the top edge of the barrel. I also routed a half inch deep circle to fit the garbage disposal.

The drainage pipe of the garbage disposal unit is aimed to hit the middle of the barrel. The funnel was made special to fit the 3" opening on the disposal unit. Two washers are welded inside the funnel for the water pump hose to fit thru. The purpose of this set-up is to recycle the water required to run the disposal, and to make the slurry.

It takes about an hour to get about 3" of slurry, but is useful for making experimental bricks or small amounts of papercrete as needed.

This is an adaptation of Mike McCain's garbage disposal grinder. Here are Paul's instructions for building one:

To make one, you need a plastic barrel with a lip; a garden water pump; a garbage disposal unit; a board (a little longer than the barrel and about half as wide); and a water faucet.

Saw the barrel in half; invert the half with the lip. This will be the top. The lip will fit over the other half.

Drill a hole in the bottom half, 2-3" from the bottom for the faucet. Plumber's putty or tape will seal it in. This

The top three racks inside the solar dryer are made out of old skids. The bottom is an aluminum tray, with a barrel underneath to catch any water which might accumulate.

Papercrete Perspectives
Part 3

BLENDER EXPERIMENTS

Papercrete concepts are easy to understand if you mix up small batches of papercrete in your kitchen. All you need are a blender, an inexpensive diet scale, and a tin can.

The first experiment illustrates the basic papercrete concept. First, cut newspaper into approximately 3x3" squares until you have accumulated 1 ounce of paper. Then you soak these squares of paper in a bowl of water (blending presoaked paper is less strain on your blender). Then, add 1 1/2 cups of water to your blender. Finally, with the blender running, tear the soaked paper into convenient chunks and add it to the blender. Blend until the slurry is smooth. Congratulations, you have just mixed your first batch of slurry.

Cut the top and bottom off the can so you have a metal cylinder, and set this on a piece of window screen or on a cinderblock so that water can drain out the bottom. Pour the slurry in, let the water drain overnight, then remove the can and let the slurry dry for several days.

There are a couple of things to notice: (1) Even though the slurry shrinks as the water drains out and evaporates, the final dry product (which weighs one ounce) has considerably more volume than the original ounce of paper. This extra volume is composed of air, which explains papercrete's high R value. (2) When the slurry is dry, you can stand on it with one foot and it will support your entire weight. This illustrates that paper which is slurried, and then dried, has considerable compressive strength.

You can experiment with a wide array of formulas. To your basic ounce of paper, you could add, say, an ounce of Portland cement and an ounce of sand. Slurry this together, dry it, and see what you think. The possibilities are endless.

This blender technique is especially useful for developing paper adobe formulas. If you have a patch of suitable dirt on your site, you can make some test bricks and see which formula seems best.

When I was starting with paper adobe, I made a series of test bricks. They all had the basic one ounce of paper. To the first brick I added one ounce of dirt, to the second I added two ounces of dirt, and so forth. When the bricks were dry, Greg Jay (who was papercreting with me at the time) and I hefted them, rapped them (they were all very hard), and got a feel for what we were going to be working with. Then we each chose our favorite brick. I chose the 3:1 ratio (3 parts of dirt to one part of paper, by weight), and Greg chose 5:1. So

we compromised with 4:1. That was how we developed our paper adobe formula. Since all dirt is different, it would be very instructive to make a series of test bricks with different formulas, using dirt from your site, to get a better handle on the parameters involved.

By the way, there is an easy way to determine the clay content of your dirt. Just fill a quart jar about 1/3 full of dirt, top it off with water, and shake vigorously until all the lumps are dissolved. Then set it down for an hour or so. The heavier particles will settle out immediately, while the tiny clay particles will swirl around for quite some time. Once the water clears, you can quickly see what the clay content of the dirt is. The dirt will now be nicely stratified, with the largest particles on the bottom, becoming smaller towards the top. When you get to a point where individual particles are no longer visible, where it's just smooth mud, that's the clay.

PAPERCRETE FORMULAS

There has been some confusion about papercrete formulas, since many papercrete builders don't weigh out their ingredients—it's "a shovel of this, a shovel of that, and add paper till the consistency is right," which is plenty good enough for real-world applications. However, this tends to leave beginners confused.

So this past spring I laboriously weighed all the ingredients for a batch, and came up with an accurate formula for the version of papercrete I've been making. Here are some formulas:

Formula for Small Mixer described in EQ #2
69 gallons water
25 lb. paper (dry weight)
20 lb. cement
2 lb. lime (optional)
26 lb. sand

Formula for Large Tow Mixer (200 gallon)
160 gallons water
60 lb. paper
47 lb. cement (1/2 bag) -- 11 1/2 shovels approx.
4 lb. lime (optional) -- 2 shovels. (Lime makes the mix set up faster, and makes a stickier stucco that adheres better.)
66 lb. sand -- 15 shovels

Note: Some builders prefer to use an entire bag of cement (94 lb.) with this formula. This makes a stronger block that dries faster.

Roof Panel Mix
Same as above, but leave out the sand. Sand (1) adds thermal mass, (2) makes the slurry pack down better for a denser, stronger block, and (3) helps prevent stucco from cracking, which are all desirable characteristics for blocks or stucco. For roofing purposes, however, we want light weight and maximum insulation, so we leave out the sand.

Paper Adobe (4:1 ratio)
160 gallons water
60 lb. paper

240 lb. dirt

The proportion of dirt to paper depends on how heavy a block you want. The less dirt, the lighter the block and the higher the R value. The clay content of the dirt should be anywhere from 30% to 100%. With regular adobe, too high a clay content causes cracking. This is not a problem with paper adobe—the paper fibers prevent cracking. It is good to have at least 30% clay, since clay is the "glue" that helps bond the block together.

Always remember that there is no "one right" formula. You might have to vary the above proportions to get a mix that meets your needs. Experiment and see what works best for you.

PAPERCRETE "LOGS"

When Greg I were doing papercrete building together this past spring. Greg came up with the idea of creating papercrete "logs," and I had the idea of reinforcing them with bamboo or sticks. These are hardly original ideas—as we later found out, Shorty Inderdahl of Salem, NM had been making papercrete logs for years.

Why make blocks or bricks in the first place? Because traditional building materials, such as adobe, concrete or clay, are so heavy that ordinary mortals with ordinary strength can only lift a small chunk of this stuff at a time.

Why make papercrete blocks? Force of habit, nothing more. Papercrete is so lightweight, it is possible to make a much longer block—all the way up to an 8- or 10-foot "log."

Such a log can be easily handled by two people (4 feet is about the maximum convenient length/weight for one person), and can be sawed to length with a bow saw or a chain saw. (I use a little electric chain saw that works great.)

Using papercrete logs greatly reduces the need for "head joints" (the mortar joints between blocks), and this increases the strength of the wall. Logs can be made the exact length you need, or can be easily sawed to length. Since dried logs are pre-shrunk, you can butt them up to your door frames or window bucks and completely eliminate shrinkage.

Greg Jay holds an 8-foot papercrete log.

Corners are much stronger when you have multi-foot logs extending from the corner in each direction, rather than little short blocks.

Logs can be reinforced with cane, bamboo, or sticks. This is a good use for saplings 1-2" in diameter—"organic rebar." If you choose to use vertical steel rebar in your wall, you can lay two sticks side-by-side in each log so that the vertical rebar can fit between them.

PAPER ADOBE

As I mentioned in EQ #2, there are environmental reasons for not using Portland cement except where absolutely necessary. There are applications—such as foundations and floors—where this "liquid rock" can be marvelous to work with.

One place where the cement can be dispensed with entirely is in the wall itself. Rather than using papercrete, use paper adobe. But before we abandon papercrete entirely, let's first say a few words about the advantages of papercrete:

•Papercrete sets up fast. There is a chemical reaction in which the cement absorbs carbon dioxide from the air, and gets hard. The more cement you use, the faster the blocks will harden. In hot, dry weather (at least here in the Southwest). papercrete blocks can be turned on their sides within 24 hours, and can be stacked a couple of days later.

•Papercrete blocks hold their shape even when completely saturated with water. You can pick apart a wet block with your fingers if you work at it, but under normal circumstances a wet block stands up very well.

•If you use enough cement, papercrete is bugproof and fireproof. (The same holds true if you add enough dirt, however.)

Turning now to paper adobe. we have a substance that is less expensive (no cement to buy), and more environmentally benign (cement manufacturing releases a lot of carbon dioxide into the atmosphere, and then you've got to burn fossil fuels transporting it to your work site), whereas suitable dirt can often be found on-site.

One important difference between papercrete and paper adobe is that paper adobe dries a lot more slowly than papercrete. With papercrete, you have that chemical reaction as the cement sets up. With paper adobe, the paper/mud slurry doesn't set up, it merely dries. It seems to take forever to dry, but then it all of a sudden, it's dry. And once it dries, paper adobe is remarkably hard.

After paper adobe has dried. it holds its shape even when saturated with water. For one experiment, I placed a paper adobe block in a bucket full of water for 24 hours. I didn't know what to expect—I was prepared to find a layer of paper adobe "soup" in the bottom of the bucket. As it turned out, the block had tripled in weight from all the water it had absorbed. but I was able to lift it out of the bucket and set it onto the ground. I could have easily picked it apart with my fingers, but even so, a saturated paper adobe block has much more structural integrity than a saturated regular adobe block, which is nothing more than a piece of mud.

Here in the Southwest, a common sight is piles of adobes dissolving back into the earth. Somebody buys a bunch of adobes, stacks them up, and either never gets around to the project or has adobes left over after the project is over. The adobes are forgotten, and the weather takes over. Within a few years, and a few dozen torrential rains, the blocks dissolve into a pile of dirt.

With paper adobe, the paper fibers are able to withstand the force of the raindrops hitting the blocks (the strongest force the blocks will normally encounter), so that they will hold their shape much longer if left unprotected out in the weather.

Paper adobe, if made thick enough, can be cobbed. So cob builders take note: here you have a substance that can be sculpted without forms, just like regular cob, but it also has a considerable R value. This sounds like the best of two worlds to me.

Paper adobe can also be painted—just brush off the surface dirt with a wire brush, exposing the paper fibers, and voila, the paint will be absorbed into the paper fibers, insuring a strong bond. With regular adobe, paint tends to form a skin on the surface, and easily flakes off.

Paper adobe will hold a screw. This means that window frames, in particular, can be screwed into the adjoining paper adobe blocks with lag screws. There's no need to use wooden "gringo blocks." For doors, with their considerable torque and slamming vibrations, I would use gringo blocks anyway, for that extra measure of strength.

Many people are very excited about paper adobe. It's a great way to utilize waste paper without the environmental consequences (and expense) of Portland cement. Adobe, rammed earth, and cob are already mature technologies in that people have been building that way for years and already know what mistakes to avoid. Simply by adding paper pulp to the dirt mix, considerable R value enhancement is possible to either adobe, rammed earth, or cob. (Just plain dirt, no matter how you work with it, has high thermal mass, but a notoriously poor R value.)

WORKSHOPS

A number of people are now giving papercrete workshops:

•Mike McCain gives workshops, and is the only person we know of who is selling paper adobe blocks. For more information, give him a call at 505-531-2201. (We talked to Mike not long ago and he is not making blocks commercially at this time. Instead, he is working on a mega-mixer. His latest project is a 5-yard cement truck, which he loads with a Bobcat. With it, he can make 350 blocks at a time. We don't know how long this developmental phase will last (and neither does he), but we would expect that he will get into serious block production before long.)

•Don and Jacque at WindTree Ranch near Douglas, AZ are giving workshops. Contact information for them is printed on page 11 of this issue.

•Talmath "Tumbleweed" Mesenbrink of Crestone, CO gave a series of workshops this summer. Unfortunately, this issue will be coming out after the workshops are over. But he will probably be giving more. Call him at 719-256-4197, or email him at <tumbleweedsworkshop@usa.net>.

•Laura and I have penciled in a workshop for next spring, probably late March. More details will be available in a future issue of EQ, or on our web site.

MIXERS

We bought one of Mike McCain's state-of-the-art tow mixers for $350 in May, and have made hundreds of blocks with it. It has several innovations:

•**Plastic tank.** Being flexible, this will presumably stand up to vibration better. Steel tanks tend to crack after a year or so, due to metal fatigue—they are designed, after all, to just sit quietly in one spot, filled with water.

•**Large opening in the bottom.** Mike used a 12" sliding irrigation gate. This is a big improvement over smaller openings, but even so, the last 1/3 or so of a load has to be "helped" out the opening with a shovel. We like to make thick slurry, since it shrinks less, and would love to find an automatic, low labor way of getting all the slurry out.

•**A way to add oil to the differential.** One problem with tow mixers is that slurry water gets into the differential, causing it to eventually freeze up. Mike drilled a hole into the axle and threaded a steel pipe with a cap into it. This allows an easier way to drain off the excess water and add new oil as needed. Probably the ultimate solution would be to install grease zerts so that the differential could be filled with waterproof grease.

When Greg and I were in full production mode, we were able to mix about one load an hour (24 blocks) on a sustained basis. But we were backing the mixer over the forms, opening the valve, and shoveling the slurry into the corners of the forms. This was more time-consuming physical labor than we would have preferred.

Mike McCain has a large open area in Columbus, NM where he is making paper adobe blocks with a steel drag form. In EQ #4, page 25, we printed two pictures of his earlier version, which makes four rows of blocks side-by-side. His newest version makes two rows of bricks. (He probably had trouble getting the slurry to spread adequately across the wider form, hence the new, narrower design.)

When the load is mixed, he attaches the drag form to the mixer, opens the valve, and drives slowly forward, towing both the mixer and the drag form behind him. The slurry is automatically smoothed on top by a steel plate. He ends up with a long ribbon of slurry, which he cuts into blocks with a cutter he designed. With this system, he says he can produce 100 blocks an hour. The concept used here is identical to that described in EQ #1, pages 8 and 9, only this time it's automated.

I have mixed feelings about my tow mixer. It certainly mixes up a fine batch of slurry, and at 200 gallons per batch we're talking serious production. But getting the slurry out of the mixer remains too labor-intensive for my taste. Also, my truck is not happy being the tow vehicle. It's a splendid old antique 1965 El Camino, with a 283 V-8. Towing the mixer down the road at 8 miles per hour (the fastest the mixer wants to go), the engine is barely turning over in first gear, and second is too high a gear. So the engine is lugging

Mike McCain designed this steel block cutter that automatically marks the location of the next block. Notice the steel drag form in the bottom of the picture—it is two blocks wide, and 20 feet long.

along, fouling the plugs, and I hate to abuse my truck like that. Greg says that a smaller vehicle, that would need to be revved up to a higher rpm to tow the mixer, would be a better choice.

I remain convinced that the tow mixer, while fine for the small professional builder or amateur hobbyist, is just the first step along a path that will ultimately lead to huge, stationary mixers that you fill with a forklift. The slurry would automatically drain out, or would be pumped out, into an array of forms. Such a mixer would produce thousands of blocks a day, with very little physical labor involved.

At the other end of the spectrum, people are having good luck making slurry in cement mixers, using shredded paper. I have been out of touch with the technological advances in the shredding industry—when people spoke about "shredded paper," I always assumed long strips about 1/4" wide. But Shorty Inderdahl brought us some bags of shredded computer paper he got from a local bank, and I was impressed by how finely the paper was shredded. One type of shredder chops the paper into pieces about 1/8" wide and 5/8" long, and the other type pulverizes the paper into tiny bits only 1/16" wide and 3/8" long. Either type would work very well in a cement mixer. The common "two bagger" cement mixers have a rather small capacity for serious block production, but they have the advantage of being easily available. They would be great for making stucco, since you would be able to use an entire batch before it starts to set up. With a 200-gallon mixer, it's hard to apply that much slurry onto a wall before it starts to lose its prime stucco quality.

FLAME TESTS

After we performed the strength tests at NMSU (see page 21) we had plenty of broken fragments left over, so I performed some flame tests on them. All the papercrete formulations listed on page 21 burned. These had a nonflammable (cement and sand) content ranging from 44% (the roof panel mix) to 65% (the formula for large tow mixer). Pure paper pulp produced a lot of smoke; of the papercrete samples, the higher the cement content, the less smoke was produced.

I also flame tested my paper adobe test bricks. The 1:1 (dirt:paper; 50% nonflammable) and 2:1 (67% nonflammable) bricks burned. The other bricks, starting with 3:1 (75% nonflammable) and ending with 5:1 (83% nonflammable) did not burn.

Flammability evidently depends on the ratio of flammable to nonflammable material. For a nonflammable formula, the critical level of nonflammable material is between 67-75%. A little bit of further testing should allow us to accurately pin down this figure.

—Gordon Solberg, Editor

A row of paper adobe blocks made with Mike McCain's drag form makes an impressive sight as it disappears into the horizon. For scale, note Greg Jay, standing about halfway down the row, and his son Justin, the tiny figure in the far distance. There are several hundred blocks in this row.

111

COMBUSTION TESTING ON PAPERCRETE MIXES

Robert Secrest

Over the past few months, I have been conducting some tests aimed at getting data that can be used to assess combustion hazards for various papercrete formulas. This is a brief report on the results to date.

I will save the details of my preparation methods for a full report. It will suffice here to say that care was taken to accurately weigh the components of the mixtures and to prepare and test the samples in a consistent manner. A propane torch flame held at one point on the sample for 60 seconds was the ignition standard used. This is much like tests used by fire safety inspectors.

PLAIN PAPER PULP

Samples made using nothing but newspaper pulp continued to flame for 30 sec. to 1 min. after removal of the ignition source. The flame spread was fairly slow. After the flame extinguished, the samples continued to smolder in a way similar to charcoal in a barbecue. Some samples self extinguished after a time. Others were completely consumed, leaving a residue of white ash and unburned carbon.

PAPER PULP with BORIC ACID

As a theater person, I have used boric acid as a fire retardant on scenery. I felt it was worth testing in this context. I added a quantity of boric acid to some samples of plain paper at 20% boric acid by weight to the dry paper. These samples did not support flame at all after the ignition source was removed. They continued to smolder and produce smoke for about a minute after, but soon self extinguished completely. Boric acid is clearly effective as a fire retardant, but represents an added step and cost factor (even when purchased as common roach powder). I have not, as yet, established the minimum effective ratio for this additive. It is possible that a saturated solution applied to the surface like paint would also be effective.

MIXTURES CONTAINING PORTLAND CEMENT

In spite of being the most popular formulae for paper based blocks, the cement mixtures are the most troubling in terms of combustion. Samples containing moderate amounts of cement (50% and 100% by weight to dry paper) all exhibited the intense flameless combustion, which I refer to as "slow burn." Unlike ordinary combustion, which produces smoke and a visible flame, the "slow burn" produces a great deal of heat, (and I suspect Carbon Monoxide) while showing no flame and little smoke. The process is tenacious and will continue to run through every sample until it is completely reduced to a light brown ash. Quenching the sample in water is about the only way to extinguish this reaction. Samples containing a portion of sand equal in weight to the cement showed no difference with respect to the burn. I have not yet tried samples with high ratios of cement (2:1 and 4:1). These levels, while of interest to the tests, would probably represent impractically high ratios in block production.

I also made samples containing an equal quantity of Portland cement and paper (by weight), to which I added 20% boric acid. In this case, the samples did burn, despite the addition of boric acid.

One should bare in mind that, in spite of this disturbing evidence on cement formulae, the ignition method used represents a rather intense starting energy level. The risk of ignition in our applications may be acceptable.

This testing is to be ongoing and I hope to have a wider range of results to report on later this year. I am quite interested in clay/paper mixtures, which show much promise.

I am happy to accept questions, comments, and suggestions by e-mail at <pptmotion@hotmail.com>.

Thanks to the Solbergs for including my report in EQ.

ROOF DESIGN *(continued from p. 102)*
bars below the curved ribs. These provided additional strength during the construction process, and were later removed.

During the workshop, about 2" of slurry was poured onto the cane. The excess water poured through the cane like a shower—it was a spectacular sight. In this photo, Greg Jay and workshop participants are smoothing the slurry with trowels.

(Continued on p. 132)

Papercrete Strength Tests

In May we had the good fortune to meet Kenneth Leitch, a graduate student in Civil Engineering at New Mexico State University, who agreed to do some compression and tensile strength tests for us. We made samples of 5 different formulations, and met with Kenneth on August 19 at NMSU's Civil Engineering materials testing lab, where we tested them with a couple of Tinius Olsen multitesters, which are essentially huge hydraulic presses with calibrated dials that tell you how much pressure is being applied.

For the compression tests, we had made papercrete cylinders, 6" in diameter, and 12" tall. The cylinders of pure paper pulp were only 10" tall, because of excess shrinkage.

Here are the formulas we used:

#1. Pure paper pulp (newsprint).

#2. 1/2 bag of cement in a 200-gallon batch; no sand. This is the "roof panel mix" described on page 16 of this issue.

#3. 1/2 bag of cement + sand. This is the "formula for large tow mixer" on page 16.

#4. Identical to #2, but with a full bag of cement rather than 1/2 bag.

#5. Paper adobe, using the formula on pages 16-17.

We made three cylinders of each formula. One of the paper adobe cylinders broke when wet, so we only tested two cylinders of this formula.

When testing these cylinders, we noticed how elastic papercrete and paper adobe are. Under a compressive load, they behave more like wood than like concrete. Wood, when subjected to moderate compressive loads, will compress down without breaking. Concrete, on the other hand, will retain its original shape as pressure is applied, until it eventually breaks.

Papercrete/paper adobe behaved like an accordion—we could compress the cylinders from their original 12" down to about 9" when we got to the 85 psi range, but they would regain about half of this when the pressure was released.

We decided to measure how much pressure was required to compress each sample by 2". Here are our averages:

#1	59 psi
#2	68
#3	74
#4	86
#5	143

As one would expect, the higher the non-elastic content (cement, sand, or dirt), the more pressure is required to deform the sample.

We then took one cylinder of each formula to a larger multitester to see if we could destroy them. This unit was set up for concrete testing and had a limited range of motion, and couldn't smash samples 1-3 small enough to cause them to fail. (For example, we applied 12,000 pounds of force (424 psi) to the pure paper sample, and compressed it from its original 10" down to 3 1/4". When the pressure was released, it rebounded to 4 3/4".)

Samples 4-5, more brittle with a higher non-paper content, did fail. #4 failed at 248 psi, and #5 failed at 212 psi. (After the pressure was released, samples 4 and 5 were both 8 1/2" tall—3 1/2" less than their original height.)

The formula for #4 is similar to that used by Mike McCain; the "260 psi" figure we've been quoting in EQ is based on a compression test he had done in Alamosa, CO (EQ #1, p. 13). Considering the range of experimental error (a single test done on two different samples), the 248 psi figure we obtained at NMSU is equivalent to the 260 psi we've been quoting all along.

But—and this is an important issue—long before papercrete and paper adobe lose structural integrity, they will compress down as more pressure is applied. So rather than asking, "At what pressure will papercrete/paper adobe lose structural integrity," a more immediate question would be, "What level of compressional shrinkage is acceptable?" If you put X amount of weight on top of a wall and it squeezes down by Y inches, is this acceptable?

The papercrete pioneers would answer: Yes of course it is acceptable. In the real world, the weight of the wall itself is insufficient to compress the bottom layers at all; even adding the heaviest possible roof (vigas, heavy planks, etc.) will not compress the wall much, if at all; any compressional shrinkage can be easily compensated for, and the structural integrity of the wall will not be compromised.

From the point of view of structural engineers and building codes people, who are used to dealing with inelastic wall systems, there might be some issues here. I think that straw bale walls, which surely compress a little when heavy loads are applied to the top, could provide a precedent. It might well be that more conservative building codes will insist that papercrete be used only as infill with post-and-beam walls. However, I remain convinced (and I think that most seat-of-the-pants papercrete experimenters would agree) that load-bearing papercrete and paper adobe walls are perfectly safe, particularly if they are reinforced with rebar.

For the tensile strength tests, we made little beams, 30" long with a 3x3" cross section. We supported these beams on their ends and applied a load in the middle. As expected, papercrete had a low tensile strength, much like unreinforced concrete. Samples 1 and 2 could support approximately 20#; the other three samples could support approximately 40#. Kenneth told us that a piece of wood this size could support 1000#. So clearly, tensile strength is not papercrete's strong point.

The conclusion to be drawn from all this is that papercrete/paper adobe are unique materials, with much more compressive strength than tensile strength. I wish we had tested to see how much pressure was necessary to cause the samples to deform even slightly, since I know that people will be asking this question. My sense is that any kind of stable (non-earthquake) real-world loads will cause, at most, only a slight deformation, not enough to be concerned about. But I think that further testing is called for, because I know that the elasticity of papercrete/paper adobe will be of concern to people who are used to working with perfectly rigid materials.

LETTERS

I thoroughly enjoyed issue No. 3. I read it cover to cover and shared it with friends!

Aleks Webster
Tempe, AZ

The first 3 issues exceeded my expectations. Keep up the good work!

Dan Williams-Capone
Parsons, KS

When I read the editorial in issue 3, I was glad to hear that you did have a spiritual dimension to your work. I do not think anything really does well without this dimension added, at all levels of our work and life.

I have connected with Mike and Sean at City of the Sun. I am really impressed with their ideas. Two of the most creative people I have ever met.

Peggy McKeown
Deming, NM

Thanks so much for your wonderful and encouraging publication. I'm looking for others who have the vision and passion to work together to use this great papercrete technology and other ideas to build with recycled products. I've thought it might be worth considering developing a recreational and educational area with cabins. Then there is a place to live, a place to enjoy, a place to make a living, and, most of all, a place to be together. Are there others out there who might like to connect on a venture like this?

I've taken several trips to find a good location and haven't settled on anywhere yet. Where have others found that might be spectacular to settle into and build a papercrete village? I'd love to find a place that has natural beauty and people open to alternatives. I'm wide open to others' dreams and ideas.

It seems like it might be time to manifest and come together. In the big picture, after getting situated personally, I've always wanted to develop a way to extend help somehow to the homeless and low income so that we all can be empowered to build our own homes and be free to an eternal mortgage payment. If there are others out there who might like to team up to build homes and lives together, I would certainly love to hear from you. I've felt like I've been on a deserted island with my ideas and experiments with building with recycled materials.

I can also see potential in using papercrete as a sculpture medium. Has anyone given that a try?

By the way, I bought a shredder (Fellowes Powershred PS 60CC) that cross shreds. I really like it. I'm experimenting to see if it makes blocks with the same integrity as the ones made with the paper slurry. Has anyone else worked with shredded paper? I'd be interested in hearing how it worked for you.

My vision has always been to develop a little community of like-minded people. If working together sounds interesting, fun or even vital, please get in touch. I would love to hear from you.

Your publication has been a great encouragement to me. Thanks so much.

Kristi Cadwell
1502 Sanford
Richland, WA 99352
(509) 943-0562

Thanks for all the care, attention and commitment you put into each issue of **Earth Quarterly**.

With the mild winter, we have moved along with the early spring and planted chard, potatoes, snow peas and onions earlier than usual. Daylilies are 6 inches tall and California poppies have sprouted numerously, promising an abundance of beautiful golden blooms in summer.

Chester McQueary
Denver, CO

I enjoyed the messages in issue #1—great job! I look forward to building with some of these techniques.

Warren W. Raysor
Dallas, TX

My sister, Barbara Kerr, sent me a copy of your #3 issue which had an article about her. It was interesting and well written and I learned some things even I (who has known her all her life) did not know. The whole issue was intriguing—I read it cover to cover.

Gwynne Smith
Wilmington, DE

We really enjoyed the interview with John Jeavons in EQ #3 and are looking forward to future issues.

Ken and Karen Potter
Albuquerque, NM

You guys crank. I enjoyed the article on the cordwood mud dome. Everybody's got what we need when we just look around us. Gordon, I thought I was reading my own

writing when I read your article on "StrawBale Waste." I had written an almost identical letter to *The Last Straw* although I never sent it. We are not ready to be perfect disciples of sustainability. Whew. Thank god... expectations breed frustration. Too fast and thorough a cleanse is hard on the system. But by all means let's be honest with ourselves: natural agriculture relies on recycling; we can grow straw sustainably by harvesting every other row and mulching what's left when we are able to value health as much as profit. I'm a big mulcher. Never till any more. Disturbing the soil disturbs me. The hardest thing for me to accept is that I can do everything less and still be OK. The New England work ethic is strong even out West.

Kaki Hunter
Moab, UT

I enjoy the articles on community and hints about <u>where</u> critical masses of community minded folks may be. Thanks!

Stephanie Weigel
Fort Collins, CO

Check out the "Ecopeasant Chronicle" page on our web site for more community info.

The newest mag is even better than I expected—keep up the good work! It is the only magazine in this house that gets read cover to cover every edition. I especially loved "Our Spiritual Gym" and have passed it on to several friends.

Now for the REAL reason I'm writing. I found a GREAT use for all those old experimental blocks that end up just lying around 'cause they won't quite work for building. I used them in the garden to line my raised beds, and they are marvelous! Here in northern AZ retaining water in the soil is a real challenge, and they are a perfect solution! On my next bed, I am thinking of putting a couple on the bottom, right under the soil, sort of like a water reservoir. Well, gotta go make blocks!

Maryruth Monahan
Ash Fork, AZ

Thanks for the back issues. Received the current issue today, and haven't yet read it, except for Laura's incredible Spiritual Gym, but I KNOW it will be outstanding...

Your objective approach to Fibrous Cement/Papercrete is great! We are leaning more and more toward this medium, as we learn from your publication. Since we will be building our structure near Rodeo, NM (Hidalgo County), and we are now in N. Idaho, I am completely unaware of the attitudes/requirements of the county building department, but will probably take an oblique approach to see how they feel, and IF.

I have been communicating with Peter Chrissanthis, who is the marketing/sales director of Progressive Builders, representing CERAMA-TECH. which I am investigating as a means of 1) Increasing insulation, 2) Waterproofing, and 3) Fireproofing/retarding. Haven't calculated the cost of using this product on our small proposed structure, but, if you don't know of it, they are on the web: <www.progressivebuilding.com>, and his email address is: <peterc@progressivebuilding.com>. I'm sure he will be happy to send you a packet of info. Mine just arrived, and even though I don't understand all the specs, it shows me that it is GOOD. Peace and Blessings,

Orin Bridges
Dover, ID

I continue to love your magazine!!! It's one of my main resources in all of the "sustainability" groups I'm part of. Keep up the good work.

Bob Paulson
Golden, CO

I love your magazine. The best part is the paper house information. I've been trying to save money to build my own house but the going has been slow. I live in a trailer right now. But I think I can make my house a dream come true thanks to you. Keep up the good work.

Edna Blaylock
Pikeville, TN

Thank you. I'm always lost for a couple of days after each issue of EQ arrives, because my head is full of schemes and questions and plans. I hope to do some experimentation this summer.

Chuck Lakin
Waterville, ME

I am a dedicated subscriber to your magazine. I'm a graduate student in the Engineering department at Idaho State University. My area of study is energy. My emphasis is renewable energy. When I receive my PhD I would like to start a center for the study of appropriate technology. Until then, I would like to offer my services in any way I can to you and your magazine. If something comes up that you need some quick engineering or laws of physics advice on, feel free to call or e-mail. I may not have enough time to do in depth research work on it but I could probably help with free advice. Sometimes there's a gap between the theoretical work on the drawing board and practicality, but I know lots of

people who are trying to reinvent the wheel and often times I can save them an inordinate amount of time by pointing them in the right direction. Good luck.

Mark S. Hall
Renewable Energy Engineer
527 Filmore Ave.
Pocatello, ID 83201
hallmark@isu.edu

#4 is another winner! Solid down to earth info. Sign me up gladly for another fact-packed year. Someday you may be wealthy enough you could send a free back issue to new folks. Should you ever reach that level, I'd be happy to write the copy (advertising) for you.

Lance Grolla
Crestone, CO

Yvonne Hansen brought issues 1 & 2 to a gathering of very green people last weekend. Much interest here in alternative building methods/materials. Articles on papercrete were so well done. Thanks.

Is the question of outgassing of toxic inks and additives being addressed? Is it a factor? Can it be sealed?

Many thanks for the excellent job you are doing.

Robert Southworth
Dripping Springs, TX

We have not addressed the outgassing issue as yet, but are working on it. As soon as we come up with anything definite, we'll do an article on it. Yes, papercrete can be sealed, but the question is: to what extent would the sealant contribute to the outgassing?

Good luck in your approach to loving the land. May your success be measured by the abundance of your yield. Good Health.

Kyan James
Bisbee, AZ

Thank you for sample issue #4. Really enjoyed it, including letters from readers, reviews, and even ads! I must have issue #3 after all the great reader feedback. A year ago I visited with Barbara Kerr at her place and have some of her materials. Now I am really eager to see the interview as well as the other things in #3 (Jeavons, etc.). Best wishes for keeping on with your important work! Very inspiring!

Barbara Conklin
Apache Junction, AZ

I'm sending you a donation to support your wonderful work as a guide/light for people to return to honoring the Earth.

I appreciate all you are doing thru your quarterly magazine and workshops and your

presence wherever you go is inspiring & uplifting.

Bless you and your delightful 'life's work.'

Linda Drew
Klamath Falls, OR
Thanks for your generosity!

Will papercrete hold up in a wet environment? Does it need rebar?

Sam Landes
Marietta, GA

With a dry foundation, a dry roof, and exterior sealant (such as Homestar Waterproofing Sealer), papercrete should hold up anywhere. I speak about this at length in EQ #2.

It would be a good idea to use vertical rebar every 4 feet or so, though it isn't absolutely necessary in non-earthquake areas.

Why is issue #15 of DCN a taboo subject?

Jorge Velázquez
Pigeon Forge, TN
You want me to give away such a good secret?

I have just finished reading all the information on your website and am overwhelmed. I am enthusiastic about your ideas and the presentation of real solutions and real ideas for living in tune with ourselves and with a more natural and positive way. I can't wait to read what you have in the upcoming issues. I am sure that they will help stimulate my already active imagination on building and living with the Earth. Thanks for your efforts.

Del Woodruff
Yukon, OK

Love the book & mag—showed to several of my contractor friends—same comment—Great idea, skip the "costs next to nothing" headlines—stress that papercrete is a durable, low toxic, beautiful material instead!

Martin Jelenc
Belleville, WI

We're still waiting for somebody to build the world's first $200,000 papercrete house, which will give papercrete much more credibility in the mainstream world.

My papercrete home was mentioned in **Earth Quarterly #4**. As you may know, my home had a mold issue. The mold is now gone, the house completely dry, and the roof sealed with Snow Coat brand sealant. (THE TAR DID NOT WORK!) We are now doing the finish work on that first half of the structure, and are planning a workshop to complete the dome which is attached. (The beginning of the dome frame is visible in the picture published in issue #4.) We will be completing the dome frame with rebar and wire to create dormers, and covering it with a layer of Crack Master. We will then be pumping the papercrete onto the frame with a beautiful HUGE hose that Talmath "Tumbleweed" Mesenbrink has built.

Christine Gingrich
Crestone, CO
mz.swing@usa.net

Maybe you could promote fibrous cement to municipal works depts. when it comes to burying pipes in sidewalks, etc.

B.P.
Castro Valley, CA

How can a 34 year old man who makes $6.30 an hour build a house? I really don't want the answer to that question because I know the answer. But I had to ask.

Robert Flowers
Macon, GA

I like questions like that! If you have any more questions you don't need answers to, feel free to ask.

I have "fibrous cemented" my tire house inside and out with a stucco-like mix. Used outrageous amounts of portland cement on the exterior to increase strength, water tolerance, and fire resistance. Also seems to have less of a tendency to crack/separate.

David Stebbins
Canyon, TX
LithoRTX@aol.com

I am an **Earth Quarterly** subscriber and while looking at this site <www.tdrinc.com/tdrhq.html> I discovered that this architect used a sprayed papercrete method to create interior walls in this building. Go a little over halfway down this page, almost two-thirds, and he discusses using newspaper and waterproof glue to create a medium which he then sprayed to form walls. I assume he used a gunnite type machine but I don't know for sure.

Because of the general lack of knowledge on ferrocement techniques in this country I have established a ferrocement website <www.ferrocement.net> and instructions for joining the discussion group are on the site.

I also recently became aware of another site you may be interested in, <www.sunbale.com>. These people are doing strawbale and then shotcreting the walls, finishing the walls and creating the posts for the post and beam at the same time. They then use a poured or shot bond beam. Interesting.

Paul Sarnstrom
hoh@montrose.net

I used to manufacture cellulose insulation in the early 70s. I rigged up a cheap and simple sprayer to spray it. I also made blocks. Using it without cement works fine in dry locations.

Ron Rosemont
Sherri.Osborn@gte.net

I have a few technical suggestions that might work out for fibrous concrete processing after reading EQ #1 & 2.

One, the paper might be shredded before soaking and mixing. A garden chipper or shredder might be used, though a special paper spindle might need to be devised. The paper grounds might be collected in large wire baskets and carted to storage. It will compact easily for storage.

Another thing that could make things easier is maybe line-feed mixing. One hopper needed to feed in pre-soaked pulp, another hopper to feed in a measure of concrete down the line. PVC drainpipe (8") is cheap. Churning blades on a spindle turn and mix in the pipe.

For vat mixing, placing a socket at the bottom for the mixing spindle, would allow for the mixer blades & motor to be lifted from barrel to barrel (each with a socket).

B.P.
rckvlle@webtv.net

Wondering if anyone has experimented with making forms for entire wall pour. My application is in renovating old barn and using papercrete as non loadbearing wall, just supporting roof subfloor. Any input or information concerning this would be much appreciated with this "shacking up project." We are in So. Colorado near Walsenberg.

Baba
UnityLight@aol.com

Earth Quarterly

Earth Quarterly (ISSN 1098-9536) is published by Remedial Planet Communications. ©1999 by Remedial Planet Communications. All rights reserved. Published August 1999.

Publisher: Laura Solberg

Editor: Gordon Solberg

Subscriptions: $20 (US), $23 (Canada/Mexico), $26 (rest of world) for 4 issues. Earth Quarterly, Box 23, Radium Springs, NM 88054 USA.

E-mail: earth@zianet.com

Web site: http://www.zianet.com/earth

Display advertising rates for Issue 6: Full page $125; half page $75; 1/4 page $40; 1/8 page $25. Write or call for dimensions. Classifieds 25¢ per word.

All articles, artwork and letters are most welcome. Let us know what you think! We can swap ad space for your submission. Deadline for Issue 6: December 1.

Earth Quarterly
Box 23
Radium Springs, NM 88054

Papercrete News

No. 1   February 2000

A State-of-the-Art Papercrete House in Colorado

Gordon Solberg

During the summer of 1999, Andy Hopkins built a little papercrete house near Crestone, CO that raises the art of papercrete building to a new level. People frequently ask, "Where are the papercrete houses that look like <u>real</u> houses?" Andy has done just that—with square corners, nice windows, and log vigas, this is an attractive house in the classic "Santa Fe" style.

After moving to their piece of land near Crestone and living in a yurt for awhile, Andy and his spousal equivalent, Nancy Telos, decided that they wanted to build a house. Since Crestone is undoubtedly the papercrete capital of the world, and since papercrete innovator Mike McCain spends his summers there and was available for consultations, building with papercrete seemed like just the ticket for a low-cost, high-quality house.

Crestone is one of those fortunate locales without building codes. Although the local Property Owners' Association approves the plans to ensure that the house will fit in with the rest of the development, and Saguache County requires a building permit so that the house can be entered on the tax rolls, and the State of Colorado requires electrical and plumbing inspections, the actual construction of the house is unregulated and uninspected. This is a prime reason why Crestone probably

Andy Hopkins, Nancy Telos, and their dog Annie stand in front of their 16x32-foot papercrete house near Crestone, CO. The house is at an elevation of 7700 feet; the Sangre de Cristo mountains in the background reach over 14,000 feet. Andy left gaps in the rebar in the bare walls on the left side of the building, so that he can later cut out openings with a chainsaw for more windows. Try doing this with most other building materials!

has as many, if not more, alternative homes per square mile than anyplace in the world.

Andy decided to start with a small house, 16x32 feet (512 square feet), that could be completed in one summer. His long-term plan is to eventually build an addition at right angles to the original structure, giving him an L-shaped house.

Although Andy's location, at an elevation of 7700 feet, can get quite cold during the winter, the soil at his site is essentially pure sand, with excellent drainage. So frost heaving is not a problem. He decided to build a modest, but totally adequate foundation—12" wide and between 8-12" high on the slightly sloped building site—out of reinforced concrete. The reinforcing

consists of two pieces of ½" rebar side-by-side. The foundation is dug about 6" into the ground. About every 4 feet, he inserted a piece of vertical rebar sticking up out of the foundation, to give the papercrete wall something to grip onto.

A papercrete house, even with a heavy load of snow on the roof, puts a pressure on the foundation of about 5 pounds per square inch. Since concrete has a compressive strength of approximately 3000 psi, and papercrete has a compressive strength of about 300 psi, neither the wall nor the foundation come anywhere close to being maxed out.

Andy painted the top of his foundation with concrete sealer, to prevent potential wicking of soil

Andy, Nancy, and Annie stand in front of the south side of their house. An additional room will be added to the east side of the house, creating an L-shaped structure with a courtyard in the southeast corner.

moisture from the foundation into the wall. This is a simple, inexpensive step which is guaranteed to prevent possible moisture problems somewhere down the line.

Andy built a McCain-style tow mixer, using a 40"-diameter steel stock tank with a capacity of 150 gallons. He used a 23" lawnmower blade. He welded a short length of 1½" steel pipe, extending 1½" beyond the blade, onto the trailing ends of the blade. This creates extra turbulence and insures adequate mixing.

For the walls, he mixed together 1½ bags of Portland cement, ½ shovel of lime, 15 gallons of sand, and a pile of newspapers 26-28" high per mixer load. This made about ½ a cubic yard of slurry. With the help of Nancy's son, Nathan Little, Andy found that 4 mixer loads was a good day's work, though on some days they did 6 loads.

Andy's original plan was to pump the slurry into slip forms. However, the original pump broke, and they ended up shoveling the slurry into the forms. They dumped the slurry from the mixer onto shade cloth on the ground, so that the excess water would drain out before they put the slurry into the forms. They used straw bales and planks as scaffolding. Nathan handed shovels of slurry up to Andy, who filled the

This exterior view of Andy's house under construction shows straw bales arranged in stairstep fashion for scaffolding. Notice the continuous form at the top of the wall. The forms are made of ½" OSB stiffened with 2x4s. Photo by Andy Hopkins and Nancy Telos.

118

forms. The work, though backbreaking, went pretty fast.

The forms were 8" high, 11½" wide (the width of a 2x12), and 4½ feet long. Since the slurry had a high cement content, and since it was pre-drained, it set up sufficiently after 20-30 minutes so that they could remove the forms and move them to their new position. They could add an 8" layer to the entire wall each day.

For extra strength, Andy put vertical ½" rebar every six feet. They would drive in 3-foot lengths of rebar, build the wall higher, then drive in another series of 3-foot lengths so that the rebar overlapped. Andy also recommends tying horizontal rebar to the vertical rebar every couple of feet or so, for an extra-strong wall.

Even though the walls were 11½" wide and reinforced with rebar, they were weak before they dried. It's important, when building with slip forms, to make sure the walls are adequately braced, to make sure that they remain vertical, and to prevent accidents (i.e., somebody pushing a wall over by mistake). Once the walls dry, they become very strong. Andy says, "You could drive a car into my house and nothing would happen. Except to the car."

Interior view of the partially-completed house showing scaffolding made of straw bales and planks. Photo by Andy Hopkins and Nancy Telos.

When the walls reached window level, he installed his window frames. He found that having the window frames in place made his formwork easier, since he merely had to nail his forms onto the frames and fill them with slurry. For this reason, he plans in the future to use modified post-and-beam construction—he will use corner posts, and the window frames will extend all the way down to the ground. Since the corner posts, window frames, and door frames will already be plumb and square, the papercrete work will consist of simply nailing forms onto the posts and frames, and filling the forms with papercrete. There would be no problems with potential slumping of wet slurry, or the wet wall leaning, or problems with weakness before the papercrete cures.

Andy used lots of horizontal rebar and fence posts above the window frames for extra strength, and he increased the cement to 2 bags per mixerload. He wanted to create a "bond beam effect" (an extra-strong top to his wall) above window level, since he was not planning to use a traditional bond beam.

Above the windows, Andy used a continuous form around the entire perimeter of the building, rather than using a series of short forms. If he had it to do over again, he would have used a continuous form from the very beginning, since it ensures that the wall remains plumb.

For his vigas, Andy learned that pine logs stout enough to span the entire width of the building would cost $85-100 each, but that he could buy 6-foot corral posts for $7.50 each. He decided to run a center support beam down the length of the building, which would allow him to use a couple of overlapping corral posts to span the width. So for each span he used $15 worth of corral posts instead of an expensive viga—a considerable savings.

He drilled a hole through the end of each corral post, and pinned it to the wall with rebar. He spaced these "mini-vigas" every 30". Over the vigas, he stretched 36"-wide woven "hog wire" with 2x4" openings, stretching it as tightly as possible to prevent sagging. Over this he put two layers of 1" chickenwire, staggering the layers so that the maximum opening was only ½".

A papercrete floor remains damp for several weeks after being poured. As Annie demonstrates, this is an ideal place for a dog on a hot summer day.

No way was Andy going to carry multi-tons of slurry up to his roof (24 mixer loads—12 yards), so he bought a new pump particularly for this job. He used a 2" Linco positive-displacement gear pump. It was a $750 pump, but was a discontinued model, so he got it for $250 brand new. The 3 horsepower electric motor for the pump cost an additional $320. (He bought a motor that would have plenty of power to run an electric papercrete mixer, if desired.) The pump worked fine, emptying a mixer load of slurry in 10-15 minutes, but was starting to wear out from the abrasion of the slurry by the time the roof was finished. The main problem he had was chunky slurry which caused the pump to clog. This was caused, he learned, by chunks in his Portland cement. Even though the bags had been kept dry, about every fifth bag contained hard lumps of cement as big as his fist. So he ended up having to screen the cement before he used it.

They built the roof in layers. For the first layer, they pumped slurry onto a sheet of corrugated roofing on the roof

Oblique view of the ceiling showing the center support beam, and the overlapping corral posts Andy used as vigas. The vigas are temporarily draped with plastic to prevent staining from the roof slurry.

so that the excess water would drain off. Then they shoveled the drained slurry onto the chickenwire and smoothed it with their hands, to a depth of about 1". Less than a wheelbarrow load of slurry fell through the chickenwire onto the ground below.

After the first layer dried, they pumped a 4" layer onto the roof and let it dry. Then they pumped on a final 2" layer. Their formula for a mixer load of roof mix was 2 bags of cement, ½ shovel of lime, a stack of newspapers 23-24" high, and no sand. Sand is not desirable for roof applications—it has no insulation value, and adds a lot of weight. Additionally, sand would cause even more abrasion in the pump.

This view is shot straight up to the ceiling. Notice the center support beam, overlapping corral posts, 2x4" hog wire, and 1" chickenwire. The first layer of slurry oozed part-way through the holes in the chickenwire, but very little of it fell through onto the ground.

119

Once the roof was dry, Andy sealed it. First he put down four 5-gallon buckets of Elastomeric primer, and then he covered this with four 5-gallon buckets of "Snow Roof" coating. He figures he could have gotten away with half as much primer and coating, but he was willing to spend the extra money for extra protection.

After he got the house weather-tight, he poured a papercrete floor, using the same formula as for the roof. He poured it 6-8" thick (the ground level was slightly irregular). He poured it in strips about 25" wide, the width being determined by the amount of slurry in a load. He didn't use plastic under his floor as a moisture barrier. Instead, he backfilled his interior with road base so that the bottom of his floor is higher than the exterior ground level.

The only problem he encountered was his inability to get adjacent strips to be flush with each other, because there was no way to know how much each strip would shrink as it dried. He is considering covering the papercrete with 1½" of concrete or adobe. Then again, he might leave the floor as is, and cover it with a carpet. With two bags of cement per mixer load, the floor is very hard, but it still has a little bit of give to it like a wooden floor. And it has considerable insulating value. He likes the sound-absorbing quality of the papercrete floor and papercrete walls. "The acoustics in here are wonderful," he says.

At the present time, the building is completed except for plumbing, wiring, and stucco. Andy is considering using a hard cement stucco, but he hasn't decided for sure yet. The plumbing is already stubbed in. The wiring can easily be installed by cutting grooves in the wall with a chainsaw.

The cost for materials was about $4050, which works out to $7.91 per square foot. This isn't bad, by today's standards. Here's the breakdown:

$1000 vigas/posts
  500 foundation
  300 Elastomeric
  300 doors
  350 windows
1400 cement (200 bags)
  200 chickenwire and hog wire

All told, the entire building required 100 mixer loads—50 yards—of slurry. This was a lot of work. Andy told us, "I started out by myself and after two weeks I realized this is a lot of work! I was in pain every night." Then Nathan showed up, and in 30 days they completed the walls and roof. The job would have gone much faster with a suitable pump.

Andy and Nancy like their new house. It's comfortable, nontoxic, inexpensive, the walls breathe, and it won't burn. The construction process was pretty intense, but, as Nancy says, "when you're done, you're done." It was a fabulous learning experience. For their next papercrete project, they will find a suitable slurry pump, and will use modified post-and-beam construction. This is one of the nicest papercrete houses that has ever been built. Just wait till they build their next one.

Andy Hopkins is available for papercrete consulting work. Give him a call at 801-412-9895.

Papercrete Perspectives
Part 4

ATTENTION EQ SUBSCRIBERS!

Despite all the good feedback we received, we were unable to generate sufficient readership to sustain a quarterly magazine. So we have downsized **Earth Quarterly** into **Papercrete News**, which seems appropriate, because most EQ readers were attracted by the papercrete information in the first place. There is always the chance that Laura and I might in the future put out an interesting little newsletter with a sustainability flavor. At the present time we don't have the resources to put out a full-fledged magazine without any cost-effective way of reaching our chosen demographic. We do hope to add new material to the EQ web site from time to time, so you might want to check it out periodically to see if we've come up with anything new: <www.zianet.com/earth>.

OUR NEW WEB SITE

Thanks to the efforts of Josh Harvey of Kalamazoo, MI, we have a brand-new papercrete web site with dozens of color photos. The address is <www.papercretenews.com>. We are still working on the site, and hope to get all the sections updated before long.

MOTHER EARTH NEWS ARTICLE

Laura and I have written a papercrete article for *Mother Earth News*, which is scheduled for the April/May issue. It's a basic overview, with color photos, focusing on two papercrete houses built in Colorado last year. *Papercrete News* readers will probably find it interesting. Look for it at your local newsstand or public library.

WORKSHOPS

Laura and I plan to give a series of papercrete/fidobe workshops this spring and summer. Details are on our web site, or send us a SASE. Last May, Greg Jay and I gave a 2-day workshop with 23 participants. This turned out to be a little crowded, so this year each workshop will have a maximum of 6 participants, so that everybody will get lots of personal attention.

FORMULAS

In EQ #5, page 16, I printed a list of papercrete formulas. After visiting Crestone a couple of times last fall, I discovered that most builders there are using a full 94-pound bag of Portland cement per 200-gallon mixer load.

Personally, I have found that half a bag per load works fine (though the resulting blocks are flammable), but I want to report that most people out there seem to be using a cement-rich formula, which produces blocks that are harder, stronger, and set up faster.

Dylan Roberts of Crestone built an 18-foot dome which took 2 people 2½ weeks to build (with 4-5 hours of extra help) and cost $550. His formula was 2 bags of cement per mixer load. Even in

(Continued on page 130)

120

An Engineer Looks at Papercrete

Leonard D. Jones, P.E.

INTRODUCTION

I became interested in papercrete when I began looking for an efficient and effective way to build a low-cost vacation/retirement home near Crestone, in the San Luis Valley of southern Colorado. I was web browsing for some details on conventional concrete and Portland cement, when a couple of references to the synonymous term "fibrous cement" caught my eye. My concrete search was interrupted for several hours while I browsed for more information. Eventually, I found a link that brought me into contact with Gordon Solberg and, through him, with a new material called papercrete. Learning about this new material and its potential applications has led me on an interesting journey.

Over the last year I have attended workshops, read the available literature, and toured a variety of completed and in-progress papercrete projects. I found that papercrete is a promising new material, but that some questions and concerns exist. I'll outline my observations first, then my issues and concerns, and finally some thoughts about papercrete's promise for the future.

MY OBSERVATIONS

Papercrete is a Portland cement-based product, using paper pulp as its primary filler ingredient, where conventional cement uses sand and gravel. The use of paper as the primary filler material means that papercrete can have a significantly lower density than concrete. However, since paper has much less strength than gravel, papercrete has much less strength as well.

A wide variety of papercrete mixtures have been prepared, with characteristics as outline below:

The cement content of these mixtures varied from < 1 bag per cubic yard (bcy) to > 5 bcy. (Most conventional concrete uses ~ 4 bcy.)

Compressive strengths varying from < 100 psi to ~ 500 psi have been observed. (Similar conventional concrete mixes would typically have around 10 times this compressive strength.) Tensile and shear strengths have not been measured, as far as I know, but tensile strength is expected to be relatively low and shear strength is expected to be relatively high.

The finished papercrete I have seen lacks elasticity, compared to conventional construction materials. This means that it will tend to deform permanently under load, not returning to its original shape when the load is removed.

Densities varying from ~ 20 pounds per cubic foot (pcf) to ~ 60 pcf have been recorded. (Concrete typically weighs out at around 100 pcf.)

Durability also varied with cement content. Low cement papercrete could be easily scratched and torn apart with fingernails, but higher cement mixtures were much more abrasion resistant. (Most concrete mixtures are very abrasion resistant.)

Several cases have also been reported where low cement papercrete (< 3 bcy) demonstrated poor fire resistance; this tendency has not been reported in mixtures containing more cement and/or large fractions of non-combustible fillers, like sand or clay. (Conventional concrete is considered fireproof, within limits.) This will be discussed in more detail in the section on issues and concerns.

Additional filler materials can be used in papercrete, including sand, clay, foam packaging peanuts, colorants, and others. Sand, for example, adds compressive strength, abrasion resistance, density, fire resistance, and reduced shrinkage. Mixtures with a large fraction of clay or clay soil are also used to manufacture fibrous adobe, or fidobe, a papercrete derivative. The addition of foam peanuts increases the insulation value (R-value) of the material.

Papercrete is not mixed and does not cure in the same manner as concrete. Concrete cures and hardens by a chemical reaction between water and Portland cement. Care is taken to use only as much water as is required to gain optimal strength, and curing continues until the concrete has reached the necessary design strength (usually 28 days). In contrast, when papercrete is prepared, a large amount of water is used for pulping the paper, then cement and other filler materials are added into the pulp. This results in excess water in the mixture. Most of this water drains off quickly when the papercrete is placed, leaving behind the wet ingredients. The remaining papercrete requires much time (weeks, if not months) to dry out and reach its maximum strength.

The manner of mixing and handling papercrete impacts its character. Rapid draining of excess water and vibration of the papercrete appears to result in increased density, while retention of excess water and minimum disturbance of the papercrete can result in lower density. This technique could be refined and used to control the character of papercrete products.

Papercrete has some modest insulation qualities. Limited testing indicates that typical papercrete mixtures may have an R-value of 1 per inch, with a potential R-value of up to 2 per inch for low-density mixtures.

Shrinkage while drying is a significant feature of papercrete. Shrinkage of 30 – 40% of initial volume within the first few hours after pouring has been consistently observed, and it continues until the papercrete is fully dried. Conventional concrete, in contrast, shrinks only slightly once it is place.

Papercrete is also hydrophilic, water-loving. When it soaks up water, its desirable characteristics are all reduced. As saturation is reached, strength and insulation value approach zero, and there is essentially no durability. It will compress while it's wet and may have additional shrinkage as it dries again. I observed several situations where repeated wet/dry cycles had taken place on papercrete walls. In all of them, the walls were reduced in thickness, and they were thickened at their bases, indicating that the load from above pressing down on the bottom of the wall had caused the wall to deform. Additionally, the ceiling height in these situations was incrementally reduced.

Some papercrete projects have had problems, and a few have outright failed. In one case, failure to complete the project quickly led to a series of problems that required extreme effort from the owner to overcome. In another case, failure to dry the papercrete adequately and to seal the building from the entry of rain and drainage water led to the growth of mold in the papercrete. Neither of these projects involved owner/builders who were experienced in construction. Other projects, involving owners with more experience, have had more success.

Making and using papercrete takes a lot of equipment, materials, labor, and preparation. Other alternative construction methods, like strawbale or cob, may be more appropriate for owner/builders who have limited resources. This turned out to be true for me as I evaluated the potential use of papercrete for my own building project. In my case, water is not currently available on my land. The alternatives of hauling large amounts of water or of paying for well drilling and pump installation up front are very unattractive, not possible on my limited budget, so I am now planning to build with strawbale.

Papercrete construction even on a single home scale consumes large volumes of paper. This may be environmentally responsible if it prevents waste paper from going to the local landfill. However, if the paper must be transported long distances or if papercrete manufacturing is disturbing an on-going recycling operation, the environmental benefits may be questionable. This will probably have to be worked out on a case-by-case basis.

Unless significant amounts of other binder materials, like clay or lime, can be incorporated into a papercrete mixture, Portland cement use may not be greatly different than concrete. Any potential environmental benefit on this account will also have to be evaluated on a case-by-case basis.

ISSUES AND CONCERNS

Experience:

We have very little experience with papercrete compared to other construction materials. Only a few dozen buildings and other structures have been erected, and they have only been standing for a few years, at most. Moreover, the number of problems and failures has been very high in view of the limited experience.

Our experience with "conventional" building materials is many orders of magnitude greater. Millions of buildings have been erected with stick framing, and many of these have been standing for over 100 years. Other materials, like brick and concrete masonry, poured-in-place concrete, and steel frame construction have been used for many years. Numerous pole barns and timber frame houses have been built, some before the Declaration of Independence.

We even have a large body of experience with materials and techniques that are often thought of as "alternative" construction methods. Pueblo tribes in the Southwest U.S. used adobe construction since before recorded history; and adobe buildings remain very common and popular in the Southwest. Cob structures in the British Isles have been standing and occupied for hundreds of years. Earthbag construction was derived from military use of sandbags for bunkers and for flood control. Some early strawbale buildings in Nebraska have been in beneficial use for over 100 years.

The Price of Experience:

History indicates that we are, by nature, builders – with an inherent tendency to experiment with available materials and methods to obtain the greatest shelter with the least materials and effort. When we use materials over a long period of time, we learn what works and what doesn't. Much of this learning comes through well-intended mistakes as we try to minimize. Buildings that are adequately (or over) constructed stand until they are deliberately demolished or until they meet the 100+ year flood or another major disaster. Buildings without strength or quality simply wear out or fall down. We understand the limits of building with common materials; these parameters are built into building codes, engineering manuals, and other technical literature.

We're not experienced yet with papercrete. We have only started to learn what it can do and what it can't. The papercrete buildings that have been erected to date have not experienced all the extremes in climate or in use that could occur. We do not know yet what the eventual result of repeated cycles of temperature, or wetting, or loading, or other conditions will be. So, until we have more experience and our body of knowledge grows, we should regard papercrete as an experimental material.

Please note that experimental work, by its nature, often leads to unanticipated results. A wise old construction foreman told me, "Somebody died for every rule in the (Building) Code." The Building Code is the digest of our experience, the accidents, and the problems that have been observed and analyzed. As far as we know, no one has been killed or seriously injured in an accident where papercrete failure was a direct or contributing cause. Let's keep it that way!

Engineering Data and Testing:

To my knowledge, only a few impromptu tests of papercrete's physical, thermal, and other properties have been done, none in a recognized materials laboratory using standard methods. Moreover, standard methods for testing papercrete have not been identified nor developed from scratch. This is not a problem per se, but it means that there are no recognized standards to determine if a papercrete user has achieved the necessary design objectives – i.e., is this wall strong enough?

Dimensional lumber, plywood, OSB, sheetrock, and other conventional building materials typically have a stamp on them from a recognized testing organization that provides information about the standards that the material meets. Users of materials bearing these stamps have reasonable assurance that the material will perform as the applicable standards indicate. Moreover, building inspectors gain great comfort from seeing these certifying stamps.

Locally obtained materials, like concrete, concrete blocks, sand, gravel, etc. also have specifications and standard testing methods to indicate how well the materials will perform under given circumstances. Moreover, these materials are subjected to testing by government bodies who use them in public works projects. Failure to meet established specifications usually requires re-work of the project, an expensive prospect. So, if you order a standard specification concrete mix from a local concrete plant, you can be reasonably assured that the material will be satisfactory.

The lack of standards and tests means that papercrete users have no assurance about the quality of the material. This may not pose a problem for conservative users, who have planned for adequate thickness, ample cement content, etc. However, users who are pushing to the edge of technical limits, with minimal amounts of material, minimal amounts of cement, and difficult or tricky structural configurations should not be surprised to discover that their projects fail.

Some Recommendations and Related Thoughts -

I have no particular problem with failed experiments; we can learn more from them than we do from success. We won't learn what we need to know about papercrete without more failures, in the lab and in actual situations. (Work in the lab just never uncovers the flaws and problems that are inherent in practice.) My main concern is that papercrete users should go forward with caution, avoiding any situations where failure could put human life at risk. Until we have a lot more experience, any situations that puts papercrete overhead where it can fall onto occupants should be avoided, including:

•Papercrete roofs, unless provided with structural support that will safely carry the weight of the papercrete and other roofing components plus as much water as the papercrete can potentially soak up

•High walls, over 8 - 9 feet high, unless appropriately buttressed or provided with other structural support (posts, re-bar, etc.)

•Multiple story construction

•Arches, domes, and similar structures – again, unless provided with adequate structural support, as above.

Owners of papercrete structures should maintain a high level of awareness and use their senses to observe their building frequently. Any signs of problems – cracks, settlement, dampness, etc. should be noted and, if possible, repaired immediately. If a severe and sudden failure seems possible, the occupants should take preventive measures, possibly including evacuation. In particular, users should not remain in a building that is at hazard overnight, nor should they allow young children or those with disabilities to remain.

As far as I know, papercrete has not received specific negative attention from building officials, only the general suspicion that they reserve for unfamiliar materials. However, you can be absolutely certain that a serious papercrete failure with death or serious injuries will result in negative actions, if not outright prohibition of papercrete. The long-term utilization of papercrete would be seriously hampered, perhaps extinguished. Thus, we have a responsibility to move forward slowly, with due care.

Methods for Mixing/Making Papercrete –

I have been extremely impressed with the ingenuity I have seen expressed in the devices and processes that have been used to make papercrete. A wide variety of mixers, stationary and towed, horizontal and vertical, have been documented. Some of these make papercrete directly; others create paper pulp, to be mixed with cement and other abrasive ingredients in a conventional cement mixer. Though some methods are clearly more effective than others are, most of them appear to get the job done. But the process leaves me with some questions:

The presence of cellulose fiber from the paper would appear to contribute to the strength of the resulting papercrete. But, the paper has to be well pulped up to mix effectively with the water, cement, and other ingredients; and it seems obvious that the mixing process will eventually start breaking down the cellulose fiber. So, where's the optimum point of mixing vs. breaking down the fiber?

Most papercrete users appear to use newsprint as the primary ingredient of their product. But some use junk mail; others utilize recycled bond paper, and a few use cardboard or other paper products. Does it make a difference? If so, what? Are different recipes or mixing methods necessary to obtain the best results?

Thus far, I am aware of only one attempt to produce papercrete in quantities required for timely completion of a significant papercrete structure or spraying project. This attempt was conceptually successful, but ran into mechanical problems with a key component.

Methods for Utilizing Papercrete –

Several methods for papercrete utilization have evolved thus far; all of them are very similar to methods used in conventional concrete construction:

Pre-fabricated masonry units or blocks – In this method, papercrete is mixed and poured into block-sized forms. When the papercrete has cured enough, the forms are removed and prepared to receive the next batch. Many forming methods, some quite ingenious, have been developed and discussed. This continues until enough papercrete blocks are produced. The blocks are then stacked on the foundation; mortared together to form walls. Blocks can be produced in any size desired. Most common are adobe block size – roughly 8"w X 16" 1 X 4-6" thick – and "megablock" size – 12"w X 24" 1 X 12" thick. Once dried, even the large megablocks can be easily carried and stacked, due to papercrete's low density.

Once set up to produce blocks, users can work until they have enough, utilizing their labor and other resources in a very efficient way. The blocks can be made on-site or at another location with transportation if the site is steeply sloped or if cramped. Block assembly is a simple process, requiring few tools and limited skills that are quickly learned. Once the walls are assembled on site, they can be protected from wet weather until the roof is on. Alternatively, users could construct an in-fill block wall under a pre-constructed roof.

Fabricating and drying blocks requires a large amount of space. Also, effective drying requires covering the blocks during wet weather and removing the covers when the weather moderates. Also, block fabrication should be not done outdoors when freezing weather is expected.

Poured-in-Place Construction - This method creates walls or other components by placing the papercrete into forms that have been erected on-site to hold it while it cures. It is similar to concrete construction except provisions must be made to deal with the large amount of water that comes out of the papercrete after it is mixed and placed. Two variants exist, one involving stationary forms and the other involving "slip" forms.

If stationary forms are used, required reinforcing bar is assembled, then the forms are erected and braced as for concrete. The papercrete is placed in the forms, and, as it begins to drain and settle, additional papercrete is added as required to keep the forms full. The advantage of this method is that it will result in a monolithic wall that should be very strong and durable. The disadvantages are that it will require production of a very large amount of papercrete within a short period of time and that it will require lifting or pumping all of the wet, heavy papercrete to the top of the stationary forms.

Slip forming requires construction of a relatively small moveable form that is open on one end and closed on the other. The user begins by placing the form at a point on the perimeter foundation, filling it with papercrete, and waiting for the papercrete to start to set up. When the papercrete has become sufficiently solid, the users slide or slip the form along the perimeter until it is almost off the first section of wall. Then the form is filled again, and the process continues until the first increment or "lift" of wall is completed.

When the first lift is complete, the form is raised, and the next lift is started. This continues until the wall reaches its finished height. Some special measures may have to be taken at corners, at the starting point, etc.; and wall components such as door and window bucks, reinforcing bar, and fasteners for interior walls must be inserted as required.

The walls are completed in increments, so the papercrete will not have to be mixed continuously. The lower lifts of the wall are exposed to the air sooner and will dry and gain strength faster. Furthermore, the extensive effort for stationary form erection is not required, and the forming materials do not have to be purchased or rented. However, the lower levels of the walls, with no support, will require constant observation to ensure that the wall does not go up too fast, putting too much load on the lower wall before it has gained enough strength to support it. Slip forming also causes differential papercrete settlement between layers, resulting in a kind of sawtooth wall texture. This is not a problem for walls that will receive additional finishes, like stucco or plaster, but some may not find the appearance attractive.

Sprayed Construction – Papercrete can also be sprayed using a pneumatic sprayer or "gun." This is very similar to the process used for spraying texture onto sheetrock or for stucco spraying or concrete gunniting. The spraying process requires a backing for the papercrete to adhere to and some kind of structural support for the backing. Backing materials I have seen used include chicken wire, burlap, and expanded metal fabric (or diamond lath).

123

The structure holding up the backing must be sufficient to support the backing, the weight of the papercrete, and the weight of the water included until the papercrete has drained and dried.

Papercrete can be sprayed on in layers, until the desired thickness is reached. Applying several thin layers, allowing draining and drying between each layer, limits the amount of weight that the backing and structural support must carry. Sprayed papercrete, with appropriate backing and support, can be used to create interior walls and other non-loadbearing interior features with a minimum amount of materials.

Spraying papercrete is an "industrial" operation that requires a lot of equipment. A spraying operation will require an air compressor, pumps, hoses, and the capability to produce large quantities of papercrete. A multiple layer sprayed operation requires a lot of on-the-spot judgment, much like a slip form operation. Spraying additional layers onto the project too soon, before the first layers have drained and started to dry, could easily damage the backing and/or the structural support. Papercrete spraying operations are also highly vulnerable to bad weather, rain or freezing conditions, and may have to be limited to the driest months of the year.

Papercrete Fire Resistance:

With a high component of paper pulp, papercrete is naturally combustible. Several papercrete fires have been reported, and some testing has been done. Some reports include a situation called "slow burn" that may be a major barrier to papercrete use. In one reported instance, a well-dried papercrete block was set on fire by welding sparks. The user sprayed down the block with water, apparently extinguishing the fire, and left the scene. The next morning, when he returned, he found the block completely reduced to ash. This and similar instances indicate that it may be possible to sustain a fire within papercrete that is not obvious to the casual observer.

It has been suggested that low-density papercrete may have enough insulation value to retain combustion-level temperatures even when the external fire is being sprayed. Low-density papercrete may not contain enough Portland cement to provide a fire-resistant coating to the paper pulp contained therein. Furthermore, the low-density papercrete may be sufficiently permeable to allow air to flow into the area where the fire continues to burn. This phenomenon has not been reported in papercrete that has a cement content of 4bcy or more, or that contains a large fraction of sand or clay.

In view of the reported instances, I strongly suggest that users should plan on mixing and using papercrete with a large sand and cement component. If low-density papercrete is used, it should be enclosed away from human habitation by a fire-resistant barrier, like sheetrock or gypsum plaster, with a fire rating of 1 hour or more. A fire resistant barrier should also protect Papercrete exterior components, particularly in areas subject to brush or forest fires. In the event that a papercrete fire does occur, I suggest that the fire department should remain on-scene until it is certain that the fire has been extinguished. It may be necessary to dig into the area of the fire and remove enough papercrete to ensure that the fire is really out and that the "slow burn" phenomenon is not occurring.

PAPERCRETE'S FUTURE

I believe that papercrete and related materials have a very good potential future. Realizing this bright future depends on a number of things, including:

A lot more research needs to be done to validate papercrete's physical properties, particularly strength and thermal resistance.

Some of this testing should be done in an accredited materials laboratory to help establish credibility of the results.

Some standards need to be established and validated, if only as starting points for continuing work.

The environmental issues around papercrete need to be worked out and quantified. Hauling paper a long way to use it in a mixture that contains as much cement as concrete when we could get sand and gravel locally just doesn't sound like a good idea to me.

Various papercrete mixtures need to be tested for performance in fire conditions, so that we can understand and deal with the "slow burn" phenomenon appropriately.

At this point it's important to establish a repository for papercrete information, including success stories, failures, and test results. Perhaps this publication can partially fulfill this role. We need to start having some documented evidence of what works and what doesn't as well as what conditions and situations are suitable (or not) for papercrete utilization.

I think that a key factor in making papercrete successful will be to develop an effective method to create paper pulp with a minimum amount of water. This will enable faster placement, less drainage and shrinkage, faster curing and drying, and more consistent results. This could be done either by developing a pulping method that requires less water or by developing a method to de-water the pulp after the initial mixing process. Existing methods and equipment used by the paper industry might bear looking into.

Larger scale manufacturing methods for papercrete need to developed and refined:

I'd be very interested to see a papercrete block plant that would incorporate continuous paper pulping, pulp de-watering, continuous block casting, and water recycling in a plant that also has a large area under cover for block drying. Such a plant could be moved from one location to another, manufacturing enough blocks in one place for a large number of houses and other structures.

I'd also like to see a trailer-mounted mobile plant with a mixer, pumps, and a compressor/sprayer that could be readily moved from one site to another for large formed or sprayed construction jobs. This would allow completion of on-site construction without the extremely large amount of heavy manual labor that is required to make papercrete and move it into the forms or the sprayer.

We need to see more papercrete projects completed quickly, with a much smaller window of vulnerability for problems to occur. This probably means that reduced water methods of papercrete mixing must be found or that drying methods must be greatly improved.

I also feel that some well-designed and executed work on spray constructed dome and arch structures would be fruitful. These kind of structures depend primarily on compressive strength – which is, relatively speaking, one of papercrete's strong points.

Right now, I feel that fidobe has the most potential for producing successful results. It is much closer to its analog, regular adobe, than papercrete is to conventional concrete. There is a large body of accepted design theory and successful practical application with regular adobe that can be readily extended to fidobe. We need a lot more knowledge and experience about papercrete before it will reach the same level of confidence.

Leonard D. Jones is a registered Professional Engineer in the State of Colorado. He is currently employed as a project manager for a large telecommunication company, but maintains a part-time consulting practice specializing in alternative design and construction as well as energy engineering for high technology facilities. Jones currently resides in Littleton, CO and is planning a small off-grid house to be constructed at Crestone, CO. His e-mail address is: <ldjones@innotech.cnchost.com>.

A Large Papercrete House Being Built in Cornville, Arizona

Tim Pye

In 1999, my wife Cathryn and I designed our new home in Cornville, Arizona (90 miles north of Phoenix) using papercrete. Now that the house is well underway, we thought that *Papercrete News* readers may find some interest in what we have experienced thus far.

The house is what I consider large, over 3000 sq. ft., hacienda style with an "open to the sky" interior courtyard. Cathryn designed the layout, based on the principles of Feng Shui, and I designed all the systems, based on the principles of Permaculture. We are "off the grid" with photovoltaics and are incorporating as many other Earth-friendly construction details as possible, such as being partially earth-bermed, having rain water catchment off the roof into homemade ferro-cement water tanks, utilizing greywater irrigation, radiant floors using solar batch water heaters, passive solar design for heating and cooling, and 12" papercrete walls. The floor will have a 4" papercrete base, then the radiant floor tubing with a 2" concrete cap (I'm excited about the floor! Walking on it should sound and feel very different, and energy efficient too).

Many of our construction materials such as lumber and plywood have come from a demolition company in the area that likes to recycle and make a buck or two in the process. Our friends and neighbors have given us some very usable fixtures and appliances (not to mention paper), to at least move in with. In rural areas recycling usable materials is the way, unlike the big cities that throw it away. A friend of mine is a "Master Scavenger" who regularly gets perfectly good materials for free or next to nothing. His secret is: Keep your eyes open... and don't be afraid to ask.

THE CODE

So..., I went to the Yavapai County Building Dept. with our plans (that we did ourselves) to build a post-and-beam single story house with "fibrous cement" infill for walls. The first words that came out of their mouths were, "We are all for 'alternative building materials'; let's see what you have." Anyway, to make a long story shorter, they accepted the plans and called us back in a week with about ten questions we had to answer. Like, what's it made of, who invented it and when, where has it been used before, what tests have been done, etc. What I did was take them a copy of *Earth Quarterly* #1, Kelly Hart's sampler video, and a baseball-size sample they could toss around. I had highlighted all the appropriate sections in Issue #1 in answer to their questions.

A week later they came back with another list. The Chief Engineer of Yavapai County wanted me to substantiate the claims about compression, fire resistance, and lasting durability. They also wanted to borrow the video to show in the next meeting for all the inspectors of Yavapai Co. (They got a kick out of it, and it also seemed to generate some credibility to "alternative" ways to build.)

While not having much to spend on testing, I went to a geological engineer in Flagstaff to test a sample for compression. To my surprise they were quite familiar with fibrous cement. In fact he told me exactly what it was going to do. I have included the test report below for the records. Additionally, he told me that he had tested a sample that was totally soaked with water and the results were the same!

For the fire resistance, I had a totally dry cubic foot block that I used for the test. I set up a video camera and a propane torch on the sample, turned the torch on full blast with the tip of the blue flame touching the block, for an hour and two minutes. It was a real exciting video. I taped the results also. It never caught fire (no visible flame) and there

---

**COMPRESSIVE TEST RESULTS
FIBER REINFORCED CEMENTACEOUS BLOCK
06/03/99
TEST METHOD—ASTM C67—(SECTION 6.3 ONLY)**

Material Description: Specimen is a homogenous "fibrous cement" block. No additional internal or external materials or devices were present to aid in compression strength or tensile strength testing.

Procedure: No ASTM test method directly defines a test method for compression testing of this type of material, therefore Section 6.3,.2,.3 and .4 of the ASTM C67 test method was used. ASTM C67 was developed for Brick and Structural Tile. This "fibrous cement" does not behave in the same manner as brick when subjected to a perpendicular load. Where brick has a definite yield point, this material continues to accept a perpendicular load although the sides begin to deform as the load increases. Therefore, no failure point was defined by this test and this data does not make any assumptions as to what this failure point may be. This data was generated for information only.

Data: The test specimen was 7 7/8 inches by 8 1/4 inches by 5 1/4 inches prior to compression. Total area perpendicular to the load was 60.8 square inches.

Specimen prior to testing: Length 7 7/8 in., Width 8 1/4 in., Height 5 1/4 in. Perpendicular Surface Area 60.8 sq. in.

Specimen after testing: Length 8 1/4 in., Width 8 3/4 in., Height 3 1/4 in. Perpendicular Surface Area 72.2 sq. in. (Note that the specimen "rebounded" to a height of 3 1/4 in. after testing was completed.)

Rate of loading: Testing was complete in 2 minutes.

Results: The load was increased at a constant rate of not more than two minutes for the total test. The specimen experienced a height reduction of 2 1/4 inches before any significant pressure was observed. At this time the pressure applied was 410 psi. Once the specimen reached the 3 inch height, the load increased rapidly at the same rate of testing. The sides of the specimen began to break down also at this time. The load increased to the limit of the machine which is 250,000 lbs. of force. This is a pressure of 4110 psi. Since no failure point has been defined, no determination can be made as to the strength of durability of this specimen and no determination has been given to the application of this material.

was no visible smoke, although you could smell it burning. It produced a smoldered area 8" x 10" x 1 3/4" into the block. The smoldering was extinguished and the char removed and the cavity was measured on camera. I also informed them that if the smolder was not extinguished it would continue until the block was consumed. So, armed with my new data, I went back and submitted them to the Chief. Another week passed when I got a call to come in and pick up our permit! After all that we were jubilant to say the least. I must add that all the folks at the county office were wonderful. The engineers and clerks all seemed to know me and were very helpful and oftentimes more enthusiastic about our project than I was! They seemed to be personally very interested in what we were trying to accomplish.

MIXER

The mixer I use on-site was certainly an evolution. As your magazine has said, every mixer is different. Since we are off the grid, the power source was a primary concern. We ruled out tow mixers and such because we would be pumping into monolithic forms for the exterior and the courtyard walls, and of course the base layer of the floor, from the inside of the house. I decided to use our back-up generator for the solar system to power the mixer and design around that. Our generator is a modest 120v- 30 amp /240v- 15 amp, rated 3600 watts. I started with a 2'x4' round stock tank. Next I welded 1 1/2" slotted angle iron 7" apart parallel across the top, and two more to the sides to form a sort of "peace sign". The triangulation is strong and it gives me more room to get inside the tank. I extended the parallel pieces out about 18" to mount the electric motor.

After experimenting with a 1 hp motor I had on hand, it was quickly evident that at least a 2 hp was needed. The motor I use I bought from Harbor Freight: # 1788-0VGA Marathon 2 HP CHORE MOTOR for $199.99 . This motor has extra-high torque and "is perfect for powering heavily loaded machines from a standing start. Enclosed motor with covered reset button stands up to adverse conditions." Shaft diameter is 7/8", which is not very common, so don't forget

Looking down into the mixer. Notice the baffles, which cause turbulence and ensure better mixing.

Top view of mixer blades

to order a pulley. Volts: 110/230, Full load amps: 25.6/12.8, Single phase, Fan cooled, Reversible, 1800 rpm at no load, Weight is 67 lbs.! (heavy). The start-up amps on a motor is usually 2 to 3 times its rating so it draws a huge amount of electricity for a few seconds when you turn it on. Wired to 240v, this motor works well with the generator, even with a mixed batch from a standing start (with the particular blade I have).

The blade begins with a solid steel 5/8" shaft with a 12" pulley. I drilled a 1/4" hole in the shaft and got an extra-long set screw to make sure the pulley didn't loosen up on me. The motor pulley is 2 1/2" diameter. I found two sealed 5/8" bearings with 2 hole bolt flanges (Dayton) for mounting at Ace Hardware. I bolted one on the bottom-center of the tank and one to the top angle irons. I took the advice printed in EQ and installed a shaft collar under the top bearing to be sure the assembly stayed put.

I began with a 20" lawnmower blade (flange pointed down), but after I used it once and it splashed everything in a six foot radius with papercrete, I went back to the drawing

Side view of mixer blades

Top view of mixer. Notice splash cover, hole to add paper, and pulley cover.

board. I next made two "s-blades" ala Eric Patterson (see EQ #2 or the papercrete book) with my handy little Dremel tool and two old 10" saw blades. I welded one of them right on top of the lawnmower blade (see picture) because my "engineering intuition" said that would be cool. The other blade I welded about 1 1/2" up and at a right angle to the bottom one, as kind of a pre-cutter, but probably not at all necessary. (Note: a wonderful source of old saw blades are equipment rental companies. Their tile cutters etc. have heavy-duty blades that when they wear out they just throw away.) This worked O.K., but a lot of splash and chunks still got caught on the straight parts of the blade.

So it seemed logical to make the whole thing an "s-blade" with the lawnmower blade being the base and its flange providing the vortex action. This I accomplished with two more saw blades and my Dremel. These turned out to be crescent moon shaped to cover the rest of the lawnmower blade, which I welded to the top. I am amazed how well this

Mixer outlet. The 2" hose leads to the pump.

blade works! Oh yeah, the other parts of the equation are that I took a bag of concrete mix and all around the bottom of the tank where the bottom meets the sides, I filled in the corner so to speak with a rounded triangle of concrete about 4" high and wide. I'm probably not describing this too well, but it really helped to create a nice rolling vortex action. Also, I made baffles with two 2' sections of 4"x4"s and cut 45-degree angles on them lengthwise, then screwed them to opposite sides of the tank. I cut them at an angle so nothing gets caught up on them.

This is what I have used for about 70 batches of papercrete so far. It's very smooth, virtually no splash except little drops of water at the beginning. The vortex action is vigorous but rolling, and nothing gets caught up anywhere, resulting in a totally pulped batch. I don't even have to check if there are any chunks hanging out. The top of the mixer is fitted with custom plywood covers or splash guards—one side has an opening shaped like a baseball diamond for pouring in half-bags of portland, sand and dirt. The other has a 6" round hole for adding paper. The bottom of the

This "J"-shaped assembly allows the discharge hose to hang on the edge of the form.

mixer is fitted with a toilet flange for the pump (more fully described later). THE MOST IMPORTANT part of the mixer is the belt and pulley guard. This I fashioned with angle iron and a wooden top. It is shaped like an old style coffin and as such it is a constant reminder to always STAY ALERT around running machinery of any type. I must get on my soap box here... Safety on the jobsite should be the PRIMARY thing going on. It's more important than the project, more important than the money you may be making doing it, more important than your schedule, and very important to anyone else working with you.

Using the mixer I start with 10" of water in the bottom of the tank. I presoak all the paper, which speeds up the process and allows the paper to pulp more completely. Crank up the mixer and add paper. I tear it up a little, like newspapers into thirds, so it fits into the six inch hole and so you feel like you are doing something. Add paper as fast as you want or can, it doesn't matter. I stop adding paper when the slurry rolls kind of smooth off the side and into the vortex, but still a little watery because it thickens up later.

127

The ratio I've settled on is 1/2 bag portland, one 5-gallon bucket of mason's sand left over from the block work, and one bucket of dirt (we have a big pile from when we dug the foundation). The dirt on our land is a red clayey sand that seems to work fine. We are also developing a new well so the initial water has very fine sand in it too. With a little compaction we do in the forms and the amount of dirt and sand, our walls are fairly dense and that's O.K. with me. Then you're done. This makes half a tank or 12". Any more volume and the vortex begins to break down, and the blade starts to get noisy. Half a tank—about 100 gallons—seems to be a handy amount of material to deal with at one time, especially if you are pumping into monolithic forms. When I hustle and have all my ducks in a row, I can do 2 batches an hour—that's filling, mixing, and pumping it out.

PUMP

The pump I use is a 2" diameter diaphragm pump with a 5 hp gas engine, also known as a mud pump. The brand name is "Wacker" model #PD2B, circa 1991. I found this one used at an equipment rental company in Flagstaff. Rental companies routinely sell off their older machines while they still have value. Usually they have been well maintained. When I was there, they were nice enough to qualify me as to which pump would best serve my application. They brought out a 2" trash pump and we tested both of them in a muddy pond on their property. The trash pump had trouble staying primed and did not handle the rocks and serious goo very well, although it did work. The diaphragm pump sucked up almost anything, provided there was some water with it. It cost about $600 including hoses. The first thing I changed on it was the discharge hose. The one that came with it is collapsible and it kept kinking up and stopping the flow, so I went to a different rental place and bought another used 20' intake hose. Next I installed two 90-degree PVC elbows at the end of the discharge hose to form a "J" so I could hang it into the forms (see photo). Maybe it's important to say here that I'm doing a monolithic pour for our walls and not making bricks.

Working with a diaphragm pump does require a bit of technique. At first I just stuck the end of the intake hose into the mixer, which works fine if there are two people—one to work the intake and one to watch where it is going—but unfortunately I'm usually a one man show. Diaphragm pumps work with a strong pulsing action. It intakes, then expels, and rather forcefully. While Nature's act of procreation is quite delighted with this type movement, when pumping Papercrete you need to control it, otherwise it will tear stuff up. I began clamping the hose to the form so it would stay put. Next I installed a PVC toilet flange on the bottom of my mixer (the part that is under the toilet and part of the house plumbing), sealed it with silicone, and reduced the outlet to fit the 2" intake hose. I purchased a rubber test plug to seal the opening when necessary. I raised my mixer up off the ground about 2' with some pallets and fixed some band strapping around the outlet so the pump action wouldn't loosen it up.

This setup works really well. I am able to shut off the mixer and pump about 75% of the batch before I need to shovel and gather the rest into the hole in the bottom. If you are quick and the pump doesn't suck too much air, you can empty the mixer completely without repriming the pump. The batches I have been making are about 90 to 100 gallons, and it takes 4 to 5 minutes to empty. I am able to stop and start the pump at any time to move the hose (or talk to the people that come by and want to know "what the heck kind of house are you building?").

A word of warning: Don't try to move the discharge hose while the pump is running. It is stronger than you and may beat you up. (Anyone ever pump grout into a block wall before? It takes two people to handle that hose too.) It is wise to stay alert when working any machine, like watching to make sure your formwork isn't blowing out anywhere (more on forms later), avoiding overpours, sucking air and losing your prime (two or more people on the job makes it easy).

As for the thickness of the slurry, it really doesn't seem to matter to the pump. I've done real thick and real thin. There are considerations with both. Thin batches pump real easy but contain less wall material, and uses more water. Thick is cool—but if the pump sucks a bunch of air, you will be stopping to prime. Also, the thicker the mix the longer it takes to empty the mixer. My preferred mix is rather thick.

Some other tips I may include are about ending and beginning your work with the pump. After the last batch has pumped out, there is always 20 or 30 foot of hose that is still full of slurry. What I do is start filling the mixer with water. This automatically primes the pump again through gravity. Then run the pump into your forms for about 30 seconds to clear out the remaining slurry, then return the discharge hose to the mixer and run some more to wash out the pump. The next day, or whenever, just fill the mixer as usual and make your batch, but before you pump to your forms return the discharge hose to the mixer and pump the water left in hose into the mix (keep the mixer running). It is best not to leave slurry in the hoses for more than a couple of hours, as it is tough to get out. You definitely don't want to leave it overnight! (Been there, done that.)

As for shrinkage and the "pyramiding" that papercrete does after the water drains out, it's a matter of timing. If I have only one wall going, I just simply tamp down the previous pour before starting the next. Better yet is to have two sections—you can pour into one then the other, and this gives it more time to drain before you tamp it down. The last pour of the day ideally should be tamped after 2 to 3 hours. As that can't always happen, the next morning I pound on it with a heavy sledge hammer.

My pump has never clogged up (knock on papercrete), except for when I left slurry in the machine overnight, but even then all I had to do was blow out the hoses with water to force it out. A solid discharge hose is essential—any kinking will create backpressure and increase the probability of leaky seals. Air in the system doesn't work very well or at all. I always store my pump full of pretty clean water and protect it against freezing. The guys at the rental place recommended that or using a pump conditioner to keep the rubber in good shape while not in use.

FORMS

The very first thing I did was apply two coats of asphalt foundation sealer (that I got at a surplus store for $5 a five gal. bucket) to the outsides and top of the foundation block wall before we backfilled. This is to prevent any moisture from wicking into the papercrete from the block.

The materials I collected for the formwork consist of: ¾" x 4'x 8' tongue-and-groove plywood flooring, a pile of 2"x 4"s and 2"x 6"s of various lengths (my demolition guy often gets overages from construction sites, with some new and used stuff at way below retail), 3/8" all-thread rod cut to 18", 3/8" nuts and washers, ½" SCH40 PVC pipe cut to 12" for spacers (I've tried ½" electrical conduit too but papercrete tends to stick to it when you go to pull them out of the wall, whereas the PVC slides right out), 2 ½" and 1 5/8" drywall screws, ¾" x 24" steel form pins or wooden stakes if your soil is not rocky, and a small bunch of 4' strongbacks. (Strongbacks are two 2"x4"s nailed together at 90 deg. to keep them straight, but I've found that a 6" wide strip of plywood nailed to a 2"x 4" will stay straight even after repeated uses and water soakings and is easier to attach bracing to. Strongbacks are critical to a straight, vertical wall, if that is what you attempting to achieve).

With our project we began the papercrete walls on top of the 8"x8"x 16" grouted block wall that extends above grade from the footing, which is fairly common. (Note: We decided early on to do the floor last. Water draining from the walls would have saturated the papercrete subfloor, which is a no-no in radiant floor heat. Also I wanted a continuous insulation layer down the walls and underneath the floor.) The idea is to sandwich two sections of plywood 12" apart very securely on top of the blocks, and, be able to reuse almost all the parts over and over all around the house. Start with drilling ½" holes through two sheets of plywood so they match up. I use full sheets on bottom of the wall set long ways, and half sheets on up. 2'x8's are easier to handle and better to get into to tamp down your pour after it drains some. I drill holes starting at about 4" up from the bottom of the

Forms braced into position.

Inside of papercrete wall after forms have been removed. The pieces of all-thread, which squeeze the forms onto the pvc spacers and hold them in position, will be removed and used again elsewhere.

plywood and 4" from the sides, then about every 20" across and every 16" up. This pattern seems to give good support and keeps the sheet pretty flat after repeated soakings. Only one side needs to have strongbacks attached and bracing in place to keep the wall plumb. The other side just copies.

Four strongbacks (4' long) are attached to the back of the side you choose to brace. One on each end, but attach them half off the sheet so you can join another section with just one strongback. The other two go about 30" apart. Run the all-thread through the plywood and the PVC spacer, then bolt the two sections together and place on top of the blocks. Next, plant your stakes and attach 2"x4"s from each strongback to the stakes to plumb the wall. Attach and brace additional strongbacks to each section as you go up.

At first I seriously underestimated the weight of wet papercrete and had many minor blowouts, especially at the bottoms. So stake the forms at least every 2' or less at the base. Without good strongbacks, your forms will soon turn wavy-gravy. Setting up the forms seems to take a lot longer than it takes to fill them up, but with a good repeatable form system it seems faster to do monolithic pours than to make blocks, dry them, stack them, mortar them, etc. Our house is shaped like an almost-octagon (square with the corners cut off), so the forms fit all around with little adjustments. The

129

Papercrete wall after forms have been removed.

wall and more to scrape off. Depending how much of a perfectionist you are, it's possible to get the raw wall looking pretty darn good all by itself. I have experimented with different sealers for the plywood, and so far high-gloss polyurethane is the best, but nothing at all is a close second. We kind of like some waves in our walls. Still to come for the walls will be some type of slip form to pour the parapets after the trusses go up.

The more the house goes up, the more I'm falling in love with it. Papercrete has a special quality to it that is hard to describe. Once you really begin work with it, and experiment and play with it, all your imprinting of what building materials should be like begin to break down. It's not hard, but it's hard enough. It's not dense, but it's dense enough. It's warm and quiet and absorbs vibration. And it looks like one of those sand paintings when you pull the forms off. It's a good thing for the Earth and its peoples, rich and poor alike. So… I would encourage anyone interested in papercrete to investigate further. Very soon in the future we hope to see a site that focuses on the research and development of papercrete, and to establish ASTM testing procedures and IBCO guidelines. Maybe a grant or an individual will provide the funds to get the papercrete ball rolling.

Tim Pye's phone number is 520-567-1656; e-mail <wizardmoon@sedona.net>.

formwork is removed the day after the last pour and moved to the next section.

Other tips: At the end of the forms where the wall will continue, I cap it with a 12" piece of plywood and a 2x4 or 4x4 screwed to the inside center. This will form a "key" for the next wall section to lock into. The same is true at end-of-day pours, to tamp some sort of irregularity on top to key the next layer. Voids will develop under the spacers as the papercrete shrinks. This can be kept to a minimum by tamping around them. Splatter left to dry on the forms will stay on the boards when you take them apart, creating less

Papercrete Perspectives

(Continued from page 120)

contact with the ground, papercrete made with this formula doesn't absorb much water, and even if it does get wet, it doesn't get mushy. By the way, Elastomeric roof coating worked very well for the outside of the dome. Dylan says, "It's the best $50 we ever spent."

MORE FLAME TESTS

In EQ #5, page 19, I reported on some fidobe flame tests. I found that a 3:1 ratio (dirt:paper, by weight) did not burn. Since then, I performed the same experiment with papercrete blocks, using different ratios of cement to paper. I found that blocks made with 1:1, 2:1, and 3:1 ratios did burn (Portland cement:paper, by weight). The 4:1 and 5:1 blocks did not burn.

Notice that the 3:1 papercrete block burned, but the 3:1 fidobe block didn't burn. I think this is because with a papercrete block, the cement starts to set up before the block is through draining—the block doesn't have a chance to slump as much, and consequently contains more air spaces, which enhances flammability. With fidobe, there is no chemical reaction, so the block slumps to the maximum extent possible, and contains less air, hence is less flammable. Clearly, density is part of the equation as well as composition.

I don't feel that either papercrete or fidobe have a slow-burn "problem." Merely add enough inert material—dirt, sand, or cement—and the papercrete or fidobe won't burn. If you plan to build, make some little test blocks with your kitchen blender, dry them, and perform a flame test on them. You can easily come up with the non-flammable formula that's best for you.

Even if your core material is flammable, you can greatly reduce the flammability of your house by skinning it over, inside and out, with non-flammable stucco. Cut off the oxygen supply, and it's much harder to get anything to burn.

THE MOST FREQUENTLY-ASKED QUESTION

The winner in our "FAQ Sweepstakes" is: What about building with Papercrete or fidobe in wet climates? It's human nature to always be testing the limits, and the only way to find out where the limits are is to exceed them. I answered this FAQ several times in this issue's letters section, as well as in EQ # 2, page 22 (papercrete book, page 42).

Wet climate strategies are obvious—a dry foundation with moisture barrier to prevent wicking, roof with overhang—but what had me stumped was the question of how to get a waterproof, yet breathable, exterior wall membrane.

Leonard Jones (whose article appears in this issue) suggests using a stucco (type TBD) coating. He says, *"Several of these coatings are 'semi-permeable'—meaning that they'll soak up a little water on the outside (which will start drying as soon as it stops raining) while protecting the hydrophilic papercrete from direct exposure to water. The 'semi-permeability' also means that the walls will breathe somewhat—carrying water vapor from inside the house to outside."*

NEXT ISSUE

Our next issue will be out later this spring. Articles include: Virginia Nabity's 800-square foot papercrete addition in Cortez, CO; Bette Heeftle's twin geodesic dome home covered with papercrete inside and out; Rick Price's hybrid papercrete/Earthship bed-and-breakfast in (can you believe it?) Vancouver Island, B.C.; and a paper bale building in Chamisal, NM.

—Gordon Solberg, Editor

LETTERS

We are a small non-profit organization working in northeastern Venezuela in a low-income farming valley and also nearby urban areas. For 20 years we have been helping our neighbors with family planning, solar electricity, education and housing. The housing in our valley traditionally has been mud wattle and thatch houses. Now we are seeing more use of homemade concrete blocks and corrugated iron roofs. I would expect that the building techniques in your book and magazine will be very appropriate and a boon for people in Third World tropics. I'm hoping papercrete, fiber cement is also useable for roofing—tiles perhaps.

Our email address in Venezuela is bloomst@viptel.com. The foundation email is Turimiquire@compuserve.com. We read about you in *Whole Earth Review* magazine.

Robert Albert, Jr.
Hancock, NH

I am DELIGHTED with the Papercrete and Adobecrete book by Solberg! It is extremely informative and gives a very thorough idea of what is being done, directions for future research, etc. I had no hopes that it would be so good. Your presentation is very well done, very graphic in the hallowed *Whole Earth Catalog* tradition.

Steve Johnson
Torrance, CA

David McGonigal and I are starting a fiber cement project in Cuernavaca, Mexico. We are building a stationary mixer at the local recycling center. We'll have a direct use for the paper from the center. The mixer will be powered by a VW car engine with a 300 gallon (one cubic yard) capacity.

I will be in Cuernavaca from 2/10 to 3/1. David is a resident of Mexico.

I have a strong interest in developing a roof panel out of fiber cement. It has always struck me the many houses with the walls completed and no roof. FC roof panels will be made on the ground, probably 1 meter wide and spanning a room—usually 3 to 5 meters. Our best idea so far is a simple double T shape. I will share our successes and failures with you.

Peter Edmunds
Solon Springs, WI

Has anybody that you know of tried using papercrete in a foam block situation? It would seem to me that it may form a fairly solid base (rebar?) and allow for more options such as traditional siding, stucco, or ?, although a bit costly for the foam block. Just curious.

Darryl F. Ladago
Avon, CO
Can any readers answer his question?

I just found your website, and I've enjoyed the heck out of it. I've been interested in and investigating alternative building techniques for several years now, as well as living simply, etc. (the whole 9 yards), and escaping from corporate slavery so I could actually *live* life instead of just *enduring* it. The fibrous cement building method appears to solve some of the problems that have steered me away from some of the other alt. building methods. Actually, it reminds me of Aerated Concrete Block—a lightweight concrete block method that is manufactured from cement with a "special" air-entrapment method. Quite high insulative properties. Quite high cost as well. I don't think it absorbs water, though...

Keep up the good work. It's encouraging to see that someone is (and has) lived the life I've been only able to dream about so far. I'm educating myself, though... maybe I'll get there before too long!

Ted Lewis
Arlington, TX

Do you know if you could use papercrete for basement walls that were going to be buried? Would papercrete walls withstand the stress of dirt against them like concrete walls would?

Jim Birdsong
jtbirdsong@juno.com
I wouldn't recommend papercrete for basement applications. Papercrete absorbs water readily, so sealing it adequately would be a major consideration. Also, papercrete works fine under compressive load, but I wouldn't want to use it where there would be strong lateral pressure, unless plenty of vertical rebar was used.

We bought your book on papercrete and my husband and I are interested in this building material. I read in a magazine if you add an asphalt emulsion to the water when you make adobe bricks, it will make them waterproof. Do you think this will work on papercrete? We live in Alabama where it rains a lot (except this summer) and the humidity is high. Would papercrete work well here?

Gloria Christian
gloriajc@mindspring.com
The trouble with adding asphalt emulsion is that with papercrete or fidobe, a lot of water drains out after the blocks are poured. So you would lose a certain amount of asphalt emulsion in the drain water, plus you might contaminate the ground the water drains into, unless you capture the drain water and reuse it. With those factors in mind, I think that asphalt emulsion could be an effective waterproofing agent, depending on how well it is absorbed into the paper rather than draining out. I don't know if anyone has tried this. Maybe you will be the first.

We live on a farm and have access to 18" tall 250' rolls of corrugated cardboard every couple of months and was wondering if this could be utilized in papercrete. Is it too heavy, and what if it was shredded first?

Richard and Melinda Stovall
stovallfarms@sofnet.com
I think it would work very well, especially if it was shredded first.

I bought your book *Building with Papercrete...* it was wonderful! Congratulations, you hit a home run.

GUSUPS50@aol.com

Concerning Laura Solberg's "Our Spiritual Gym" printed in EQ #4: Without your permission I have sent this great piece of imaginative insight to friends and family. Hope you don't mind. Perhaps a condensed version could be put to print for a wall hanging, just to remind us of what really makes life livable. Thanks, Laura Solberg.

M. Wynn
Moab, UT

I've just discovered your web site and I found it very very interesting. It's simple, natural, creative. We like it.

I travel a lot, especially in Spain, Ibiza, USA and at Ibiza I met an English man, very open-minded, who created "La Casita Verde" (the Green House) built with recycled bottles of Coca, beer...

Otherwise, your technique is interesting because I go very often in Rainbow Gatherings (well known in USA) or Rainbow Communities where everything natural, creative, colored are welcome. At present some friends and I, we worked on a geodesic structure, very light and simple to build, and yours could be used too.

Kerilia and Co.
kerilia@hotmail.com

Weather is closing in here in Nova Scotia and we hope to conduct some experiments soon. How does this material respond to wet and freezing conditions?

Chris Cann
Canning, Nova Scotia

131

The trick would be to build on a dry foundation and seal the outside with a waterproof, yet breathable, membrane to prevent water infiltration. EQ #5 talks about a simple plastic drying shed build by Paul Reavis in Wisconsin to speed up the drying process. In your climate, it would be necessary to fully exploit your summer time window.

We have read your exciting article in *Living Lightly*. We are a small community in Popanyinning, 160 km from Perth, West Australia. We were about to start building some dome structures of sand bags with the design from "Calearth" when we saw your article & we prefer to work with lighter materials. Also we like the fact that one can cut & shape so easily. Thanks for a great article.

Robert Bulanyi
bmb@treko.net.au

We just bought your book and are obsessed with the possibilities. Thanks for the inspiration!

Mere and Doug
meredoug@email.msn.com

I've lived long enough now to be a little cautious (hope it's not just the UK environment!). One of my key concerns about papercrete is the damp Scotch mists. However, I'm sufficiently fired up by now to go ahead with some pilot building. I have the space here.

I liked Laura's "Essence of Simplicity" a lot.

I have just finished building a large 5x6M, 38 sectional workshop for a Norwegian friend who teaches classes on making your own natural skin-care products,

cosmetics/soaps, etc. My main interest in doing it was that he is driven by the notion that he is empowering folk to make it themselves—in an area that has been a heavy commercial rip-off for some time.

I also love to see the dawning realisation in folk's eyes when they see that they can do it, because there are so many self-interested forces out there that would persuade them of the opposite.

Something that might give folk the notion that they could build their own nest is potentially very empowering, but does need to be backed up by practical demonstration.

One more question, though... I was talking to my sister in England about papercrete this evening and she wondered why it was not utilised in "Third World" situations, such as around Sao Paulo dumps. Is it? And if not, what are the problems?

I'll keep you briefed on any earth shattering results, you can be sure!

Richard Sloan
richard@lime-kilns.freeserve.co.uk

I think you are definitely going to push the papercrete concept to the limit!

Probably the people in Sao Paulo have never heard of papercrete. One problem they might have is the high cost of cement, in which case fidobe would be more appropriate. I do know that in many parts of the 3rd world, there isn't the glut of "waste" paper we have in the industrialized world. If the Sao Paulo dumps have a lot of paper/cardboard, then I guess we need a Peace Corps volunteer with a mixer to go down there and show them how it's done.

I have moved to Alpine, TX as I said I was doing last summer. I am glad to have moved out of the city finally.

In 3 months, if all goes according to plan, I'll be starting to build a house of cards... er papercrete, fibrous cement, or padobe (as I've decided to call it). It will be about 2500 sq ft as planned now. I plan to document it all on video. I may have some new info for you in a few months, because I'm going to see if padobe can be pumped into a form using a "trash" (sewage) pump.

Here in Alpine there are at least 3 people interested in padobe. Tom Curry, who had a letter in EQ, has built a low wall in front of his studio. There may be others I'll ferret out eventually. I'm sure to stir up (sorry) a lot more interest when I build a house.

Down in the Study Butte/Big Bend NP/Lajitas area I don't know of any building going on, but there is some interest. Mark Spurlock in BBNP, who had a letter in EQ, is still scrounging all the cardboard from the park operations. There are several straw bale homes, and some domed roof building with adobe.

Bob Brewer
Alpine, TX
trekker4@aol.com

I have connections with a recycling project which collects waste paper from houses in Oxford, and was considering the possibility of manufacturing & marketing bricks of fibrous cement.

Wayne Adams
Oxford, England

I need labor for a fidobe house(s) outside Bisbee, AZ. Short-term, possible housing on site. Hourly wage.

Stephanie Kaiser
520-364-9004
stephaniekaiser@theriver.com

Papercrete News

Papercrete News is published by Remedial Planet Communications. ©2000 by Remedial Planet Communications. All rights reserved. Published Feb. 2000.

Publisher: Laura Solberg
Editor: Gordon Solberg
Subscriptions: $20 (US), $23 (Canada/Mexico), $26 (rest of world) for 4 issues. Send to Papercrete News, Box 23, Radium Springs, NM 88054 USA.
Phone 505-526-1853
E-mail: earth@zianet.com
Web site: www.papercretenews.com
All articles and letters are welcome. Let us know what you're up to! Deadline for Issue 2: April 1.

ROOF DESIGN *(continued from p. 112)*

This is the completed layer of slurry, drying in the sun. The cane sticking out at the end of the roof was later trimmed to the same length.

(Continued on p. 145)

Papercrete News

No. 2   August 2000

An 800-square-foot papercrete addition in Cortez, CO

Virginia Nabity of Cortez, Colorado never thought of herself as a builder, but she is now living in a home, half strawbale and half papercrete, that she built herself with the help of hired carpenters. Her housebuilding saga began in 1996, when she attended a strawbale workshop in Tucson. She was living in a trailer at the time, and the workshop inspired her to hire a carpenter and build a snug little strawbale house, with the trailer attached.

In 1999 she heard about papercrete from *Earth Quarterly*, and decided to replace her trailer with an 800-square-foot papercrete addition. She invited Mike McCain to give a workshop at her house so that she could learn about the ins and outs of papercrete. Otherwise, she said, *"It would have been a carpenter and me, in ignorance, trying to proceed."* Mike brought a tow mixer to the workshop and made a bunch of papercrete "logs" to demonstrate the process. After the workshop Virginia bought the mixer from Mike, and used it to mix hundreds of loads of slurry to build her addition.

The following photos by Virginia Nabity illustrate the construction process. The photos of the mostly-completed building at the end of the article are by Gordon Solberg.

Construction was started on July 21, 1999. Laura and I visited on Oct. 27, at which time the

Virginia Nabity of Cortez, Colorado adds newspapers to her tow mixer. In the background is her 800-square-foot papercrete addition, with the metal roof completed. *Photo by the Cortez Sentinel.*

walls were up, doors and windows were in, and the roof was completed except for the metal roofing. This is fast work for papercrete! Construction would have gone much faster, but work was slowed by an unusually wet summer monsoon season—it rained every day for six weeks. This created no problems except that the papercrete didn't dry out as fast as it would have in dry weather.

This photo shows Laurin Desseaux, Virginia's carpenter, standing where the trailer used to be. On the left, the frame wall that connected the strawbale structure with the trailer is temporarily covered with plastic. At the bottom and right side of the picture is the newly-poured stem wall for the papercrete walls—12" wide and 10" high, resting on a rubble-filled trench, reinforced with two strips of rebar. They inserted vertical rebar every couple of feet in the wet concrete, on which to impale the first course of papercrete logs.

Laurin carries a bucket of papercrete slurry to the floor. The floor is 6" of papercrete covered with 2" of concrete. The function of the papercrete subfloor is for insulation, and to elevate the floor so that the plumbing will gravity-flow into the septic tank.

The papercrete subfloor required 30 200-gallon mixerloads of slurry. The slurry was dumped into 5-gallon buckets, which were put into a wagon and pulled to where they were needed. Virginia and Laurin started the subfloor on July 21 and finished July 27. They then poured the concrete on Aug. 11.

In the background is the stud wall stuccoed over with papercrete. Notice the arched doorway which connects the strawbale part of the house with the papercrete part.

They removed the plastic from the stud wall shown in the previous photo, and filled in between the studs with papercrete for insulation.

Here are some of the 12" wide, 8-foot-long papercrete logs they made. Notice the wagon used to haul buckets of slurry from the mixer to the work site. In the background is the tow mixer Mike McCain made for Virginia. It is one of the last tow mixers he made with a 4" horizontal opening, which is inadequate for getting the slurry out. His mixers now use a 12"-diameter irrigation gate that dumps the slurry out the bottom of the tank. This works a lot better, but even with the improved design you have to shovel the last bit of slurry out the hole.

Virginia got her paper for free from the local newspaper publisher, the Cortez *Sentinel*. Newspaper publishers are usually glad to get rid of their unsold papers. She bought her Portland cement by the barrel—it's cheaper that way. By the time we visited her, she had mixed 150 loads of slurry and was on her 8th barrel of cement. She used 9 shovels of cement in each mixerload, which she estimates is the equivalent of a bag of cement per load. She towed the mixer about a mile and a half to mix each load. *"The mix is pretty well mixed, unless I don't have enough water in it. Then you have clumps. Like yesterday it took three trips down the road, which is funny because after 150 loads you would think you had it pretty down pat."*

After she mixed her slurry, she dumped it onto a drain board. *"My water table is high, plus I didn't want to have to spend more money for water than I had to, so I started saving the water that drained out of the slurry and using it for the next mixer load. There was probably between 20 and 30 gallons per load that went back into the mixer. I didn't want it all going into the water table and making it higher."*

The finished wall required wooden braces to hold it in place until the papercrete dried. Virginia said, *"You try to keep the wall straight and then it bulges all over the place. I was so glad when the braces came down because I kept tripping over them."*

Laurin said, *"If we were doing it over again, one thing that I think I'd want would be to run horizontal rebar in the wall every two or three courses. Rebar keeps the wall rigid like they use in concrete construction—½" rebar would be adequate. Without rebar, the walls have a tendency to want to go wherever they want to go. I was gone a couple of days and came back and the long wall was way in and I was worried that it would fall over. The wall was bowed in by 10". That's why we put the bracing there."*

Here Laurin is laying papercrete logs. For the first couple of courses, he drilled holes in the logs so that they could be slipped over the vertical foundation rebar. The first two courses took about 6 hours to lay on Aug. 16. After they laid seven courses of logs, they finished out the wall by pouring the slurry directly into slip forms.

Side view of her addition, showing glass blocks embedded in the papercrete wall.

Front view of Virginia's house. The original straw bale house is on the left; the papercrete addition is on the right. The roof to the addition had just been built, and the metal roofing had not yet been installed; those boards on the roof are to help keep the roofing felt from blowing away. After the metal roofing was installed and the papercrete addition was painted to match, the two sections now blend together into an attractive architectural unit.

Interior view. The papercrete windowsills had been poured the day before. Notice how the excess water has wicked into the surrounding papercrete wall. If the weather remains warm and dry, this water will be totally evaporated within a few days.

Virginia hired another carpenter to build a truss roof, visible at the top of the picture. On top of the papercrete wall is a wooden bond beam. Holes were drilled through this bond beam every 2 feet, and 4-foot lengths of rebar were driven through the holes down into the wall, and bent over at the top. Then the roof trusses were nailed to the bond beam. In this way the roof, bond beam, and wall are strongly attached to each other.

What about building codes? Virginia's house is out in the county, and Cortez County doesn't have building codes. This greatly simplifies the situation.

Virginia was pleased with her building and said she would build with papercrete again. She said her addition took longer to build than she had hoped for (the unusually rainy summer didn't help), and it cost more then she had anticipated—$20 a square foot, largely because of the conventional truss roof.

Laurin also liked building with papercrete. *"I am impressed with it. Not so much the speed of construction, but what the final product is. You can't get this out of a frame house. I would do it again. I hope to build myself a house out of papercrete. I have been in construction for over 26 years. I've built out of concrete and wood, and I'm impressed with the product of papercrete. It's time consuming, but..."* At which point Virginia broke in and said, *"Laurin said when we were working, 'I can't believe that work can be so much fun!'"*

—Gordon Solberg

Laurin Desseaux is interested in building more papercrete houses. If you have a paying contracting job for him, give him a call at 970-564-9689. You can contact Virginia Nabity at 970-565-1981.

Rear view. The papercrete addition is on the left; the strawbale section is on the right.

136

A Paper Bale Building in Chamisal, N.M.

This innovative paper bale structure was built in Chamisal, NM (about halfway between Taos and Española on the "high road") in 1998 with the help of a $25,000 grant from the U.S. Forest Service (the site is on Forest Service land). The building houses the Chamisal Reuse Center, which recycles household goods back into the community. It seemed appropriate to build the Reuse Center out of recycled materials, and paper bales seemed like just the ticket.

Jean Nichols, coordinator of the project, sent us a letter telling of the project's history:

Being the first of its kind in NM, our building was required to be post & beam with bale infill. This and all the codes, inspectors, licensed architects, etc. caused the building to suffer from construction "overkill." Bureaucracies are not yet in line with the 3 R's. In building up to code, we have had to buy some new materials, although the roof is almost entirely reused. We acquired lumber, I-beam, propanel and insulation by volunteering to do the demolition on a local community center rebuild project.

The building houses reusable household goods and operates as a "neighborhood exchange." Another portable building acts as a "free box" textile recycling station. It was donated to and moved by Earthmothers of Invention, a group specializing in quiltmaking and other textile recycling efforts.

We have yet to know whether the Reuse Center can operate with the community sharing in the upkeep or whether a job will need to be created. We suspect the latter. Certainly there is the potential of many spin-off businesses.

The County is responsible for regular recycling. Although we have seen nothing yet at the transfer sites, we hope that they will soon come on board as partners in source reduction rather than adversaries.

The Taos County building authorities weren't particularly helpful, and they required her to make a presentation before the State Construction Industries Division in Santa Fe. She said, *"They gave us a really hard time. They were not enthused about this project, and they didn't want to work with it at all. So they made me jump through every hoop."*

A forklift lifts a paper bale into position. Each bale is 2½ feet wide, 3½ feet high, and 6½ feet long, and weighs 1600 pounds. These are standard bales, just as they are baled for recycling. Smaller bales, which would be easier to work with, could be baled by local municipalities for residential use.

Another view of the construction process. Jean says that ideally, if you were able to use common sense rather than being forced to follow the building codes, you would dig a trench, put in a row of shredded <u>plastic</u> bales, half below and half above the ground, then switch to paper bales. Around the top, pour a concrete bond beam.

137

They drove ¾" rebar spikes through the bales to hold them together. No mortar was used between bales, but Jean thinks that papercrete would have made excellent mortar.

Front view before the building received its final paint job. The size is 22x32 feet—704 square feet. The pillars are tire rims welded together. Flammability tests showed that the paper bales won't burn, because they're so dense.

Side view. For scale, notice our son Neil standing next to the building. The space between the

paper bales and pitched roof is filled with bottles embedded in concrete, to give extra light and use up the bottles.

Interior view showing post-and-beam construction. Notice the recycled sofas and nice selection of books.

Using paper bales for construction is an innovative concept, and this building turned out very well. After all was said and done, Jean ended up with mixed feelings about the project. For starters, they were required to use post-and-beam, even through the paper bales were perfectly capable of serving in a load-bearing capacity. (Philosophically, they wanted a building that was as elegantly simple as possible, with the maximum amount of recycled materials, but the authorities nixed this.) The county people were a drag to work with, but the Forest Service people were very nice. Partly because of this building, the local Forest Service district received an award from Harvard and an extra $100,000 in funding, but not one penny of this was invested in further community endeavors. (The money was all spent "internally," as they say.) The Forest Service did, however, spend $10,000 on an award dinner to commemorate the project. There just seems to be that special something about bureaucracies.

—Gordon Solberg

For more information about this building or the Chamisal Reuse Center, contact Jean Nichols at 505-587-2200 (home), 505-587-2889 (studio), or 505-751-7972 (pager).

To join the papercrete e-group, go to the following URL:
www.egroups.com/group/papercretenews
To access the e-group archives:
www.egroups.com/messages/papercretenews
For a list of papercrete builders:
www.egroups.com/message/papercretenews/27

Stucco Adventures

This year I stuccoed the outside of my papercrete office, and both the outside and inside of my hybrid papercrete/fidobe guest house.

I stuccoed the outside of the office with papercrete. After a lot of experimenting, I settled on the following formula:

> 5 gallons wet paper pulp from my tow mixer
> 1 gallon Portland cement
> 1 gallon sand from my arroyo, screened through
>   a window screen
> 1 shovel lime (this is probably optional, but I
>   had a bag of lime I wanted to get rid of)

I mixed all this together in a cement mixer (a wheelbarrow and hoe would work just as well). This is just the right size for a batch. Last year we were mixing 200-gallon batches in our tow mixer, and there's no way you can apply this much stucco before it starts to go "off"—after about an hour the cement would start to set up. Being papercrete, it didn't get hard, but it lost its prime spreadable quality. With a small batch, there is plenty of time to trowel it onto the wall and get it nice and smooth.

The wall I was applying the stucco to was bone dry. Sometimes I would sprinkle the wall with water before applying the stucco, but usually I would just make the stucco a bit watery. I would hold this wet stucco against the wall for about a second, and the excess water would be instantly absorbed into the wall. Then I would start troweling.

The papercrete formula worked very well, but my favorite stucco is fidobe, which I used on my guest house. This stuff is a dream to work with—it spreads like butter, and stays soft long enough so the trowel marks can be smoothed off. It is a very forgiving stucco to work with. Since there is no cement to set up, I can mix up 200 gallons at a time and spread it at my leisure.

My dirt supply lacks clay, so I fortify each batch with about 10 gallons of mud from my pond, which is almost pure clay. This mud is biologically active, containing willow roots and swamp grass as well as the occasional small pebble. So when I'm troweling on the stucco, occasionally I'll have to flip a rock or a root out of the stucco with the corner of my trowel. I'm sure that fidobe stucco made with clean dirt with a high clay content would be wonderful to work with.

One thing I would advise would be to mix the slurry about twice as long as usual, to make sure the paper is thoroughly pulped. Small lumps of paper are of no importance when casting blocks or wall sections, but can be aggravating in stucco. It's not all that big a deal, really—just flip the offending lump out of the stucco with the corner of your trowel.

I have found that both papercrete and fidobe stucco adhere well to both papercrete and fidobe blocks—I think the paper fibers on the surface of the block tend to interlock with the paper fibers in the stucco. We did find, however, that fidobe stucco won't adhere to cinderblocks—it peels right off after it dries. Fortunately, papercrete stucco adheres very well to cinderblocks.

We did find occasional spots where the stucco didn't adhere to the wall—if you rap such a spot with your knuckles, it makes a hollow sound. These areas can be easily repaired by screwing the stucco to the underlying wall with 2" screws. Try doing that with cement stucco over adobe!

Last September, while visiting Glen Canyon Dam in Arizona, I noticed exactly the same concept on a mega scale—the dam engineers had essentially screwed the bedrock together at the base of the dam.

The following picture shows rock bolts applied in a 10x10-foot grid, and I have included info from an explanatory sign at the site. It's fascinating that a concept that works so well with papercrete stucco can be scaled up a million fold and used in such a large application.

Since Navajo sandstone tends to fracture vertically, these rock bolts lock rock slabs together, thereby minimizing rock falls into the canyon. These bolts extend from 45 to 75 feet into the canyon wall. They are built up in 10 foot sections. An expansion device on the end ties the bolt solidly to the wall. The plate is 14 inches square and 2 inches thick. The bolts are cement grouted in the wall.

Papercrete News

Papercrete News is published by Remedial Planet Communications.   ©2000 by Remedial Planet Communications. All rights reserved. Published Aug. 2000.

Publisher: Laura Solberg

Editor: Gordon Solberg

Since this is our last issue, we are no longer selling subscriptions.   Information about all our publications is available on page 10 of this issue.

Papercrete News, Box 23, Radium Springs, NM 88054 USA.

E-mail: earth@zianet.com

Web site: www.zianet.com/papercrete

A Hybrid Papercrete/Earthship Bed and Breakfast on Vancouver Island

The most frequently-asked question we get is: "What about building with papercrete in humid climates?" When answering this question, we always refer people to Rick Price's bed and breakfast under construction at Ladysmith, British Columbia (on Vancouver Island), which has got to be one of the wettest winter climates in North America.

When Laura Solberg visited Bellingham, WA last December, she took the ferry to Vancouver Island to interview Rick and see his construction activities. The weather was cold and gray, with a constant drizzle. This is definitely a humid climate.

This view shows the front and side papercrete walls. The long wall on the right side of the picture faces south. *Photos by Laura Solberg*

The building is a tire-wall Earthship in the back, with papercrete front and side walls. The site is drained with French drains. *"We use 4" pipe, 2" below and sloping to the front of the building and then drain rock all the way out the back, so any water that comes down the back of the building hits the drain rock and goes right down. So we never get any water inside the building. We just had a 70 mm (2¾") dump of water in 24 hours and it's moist at the back of the building but there is no running water."*

His papercrete, which he calls micro-fibrous concrete, is made using the original formula printed in *Earth Quarterly*—60% paper, 30% sand, and 10%

A close-up of the papercrete wall and doorway visible on the left side of the previous photo.

Portland cement by volume. Rick says, *"This is all experimental. There is a bow in the wall, because the concrete specialist that was helping me said that the slurry was really light and we wouldn't need extra bracing. I said how can it be light, it has the same amount of water in it as concrete. He said the pulp is light. I thought he was wrong and I was right, so now we have a bow. When you are forming, you have got to form it just like regular cement."*

Rather than building a greenhouse for the south wall, like a standard Earthship, Rick built a papercrete wall, with windows. This will moderate the temperature inside the building—it will be cooler during the day and warmer at night.

He has shredded paper delivered to him. *"The best place to get paper is from the shredders, the guys who shred documents. They will bring it to you. It will cost you, but to have it brought to you already shredded makes it easy. It doesn't have to be soaked if it is shredded.*

" Micro-fibrous concrete takes 28 days to cure (in his climate—Ed.). *It doesn't matter how wet it is.*

This view shows the tire wall at the back of the building. The front papercrete wall on this side of the building has not yet been built.

Regular concrete poured down a sonatube into the ocean, in 28 days it will be 98% hard. For the rest of the known time it tries to close that 2% gap. So cement that was poured 100 years ago is harder today than the day it was poured; it just gets harder. With concrete, 60% sand and 40% Portland, it will cure to hard in a couple of days. Micro-fibrous concrete takes 28 days to get hard and it is soft for many of those days so you can't walk on it. But on that 28th day it is hard and then it starts closing that 2% gap and that is why it works. So people who work with micro-fibrous concrete, if they have worked with regular concrete before, say ewwww this stuff is soft. But on that 28th day—PING it is hard! And it has R value and it gets rid of garbage. And that is very good."

He talked about his philosophy and plans for the future: *"People keep re-inventing the wheel. That is what my 3rd Millennium Construction Company is about—to stop people from re-inventing the wheel. American draft dodgers from the Vietnam era came here in 1967 and they built underground homes in the Cherry Point area. I was in junior high at the time and I thought they were the coolest of the cool. That's when I got interested in this. I have looked into every system there is out there, added my own logic and spirituality to what is going on here. This is 35 years of non-stop study and going to seminars and conferences and talking to people. People don't have to re-invent the wheel—it has already been done. Socrates knew all this stuff. All the old guys knew all this stuff, so why do we keep trying to re-invent the wheel?*

"If I had an extra million dollars—and I will one day—I would pick a place in the central US and I would put in a plant to manufacture micro-fibrous concrete

blocks. They are much lighter to ship, so they would be more cost effective. So you take out the blocks to be delivered and then return with the truck loaded with something else.

"You are either brain-dead or a big money family like a Dupont or a Hearst, if you can't see the warrant in micro-fibrous concrete."

The last we heard, Rick Price was planning to start up a papercrete factory in Washington State. You can contact him at 250-245-4500; <3rdmill@nisa.net>.

This is how my office roof looks from the inside. Fluorescent lights running down the middle provide plenty of light. Visitors always admire the cane ceiling.

Arizona Earthbag with Papercrete Stucco

Irv and Eve Jameson of Kingman, AZ write: *"Here is a picture of us in front of our home—papercrete roof—adobe in sandbag walls. UNFINISHED—of course!*

141

A Twin Dome Papercrete House in Crestone, CO

Somewhere back in *Earth Quarterly* I said that we would know papercrete had really arrived when somebody built a $200,000 house out of it. Well, this is the house.

At just under 2000 square feet, this house built by Bette Heeftle of Crestone, CO, features 30' and 24' geodesic domes connected by a 17' frame center section. She bought the 30' in kit form from Pacific Domes in Ashland, OR. For the 24' dome, she bought their plans and had the struts made at a metal shop in Alamosa, CO—saving considerable shipping expense.

They cut 2" polyiso board (R-15) to fit between the dome struts. They then covered the polyiso inside and out with chickenwire, and blew papercrete slurry onto it, it, using a $600 Wilden air-powered diaphragm pump, originally designed to pump sludge out of mines. This pump worked, but it had to be taken apart frequently and cleaned out. Bette said, *"The pump didn't work well at first. We would just start to get some slurry sprayed on, and it would clog up. The papercrete compresses in there and it sticks to the walls and the diaphragm would blow out. We coated the inside with teflon, so it was slick, and we got a harder rubber diaphragm. When we get done with a load we partially tear it down and clear it out. At the end of the day we take it all apart and spray down the insides. I think this*

Geodesic dome after the struts were bolted together, but before the polyiso boards were installed.

Laura standing in front of one of the papercrete-covered domes.

is probably the cheapest, most effective way to pump slurry. We have a big air compressor that you hook it into, and then one of the hoses pumps the slurry into the air pressure and it kind of atomizes it, so it really sprays it out."

They used Dylan Roberts' 200-gallon tow mixer (the kind with the black plastic water tank—there are a lot of these being towed very slowly across the Southwest even as we speak). Their formula is: ¾ wheelbarrow of paper (about 65 pounds), two bags of cement, and about 1/3 bag of lime per batch. *"We mixed it real thin. We used sand whenever we thought it*

The other dome, and the frame center section.

was necessary, like on the final coats inside for the mass to hold the heat. Kelly Hart said not to put sand on the outside coat because I don't want to hold the heat on the outside. I want it to be more insulative. So we kind of played around with the formula. We're just using plain newspaper because magazines or any other paper doesn't mush up good enough to go through the pump. We need it pretty mushy to spray it. We blow papercrete on the inside a couple of inches and with the two inch polyiso it is already R-15, so we don't have to do that much papercrete. Still, we're doing maybe 6" total."

Using the pump/tow mixer combination, they were able to spray 8 loads of slurry a day, even though they had to open the pump and clean it after each load.

When we visited in late October, Bette and her crew of workers were hard at work spraying papercrete. They were really pushing the envelope, because winter was fast approaching, and a hard freeze can destroy the structural integrity of wet papercrete. (Papercrete gets a lot of its strength from the millions of interlocking paper fibers. Freezing it before it has dried causes it to expand, tearing the paper fibers apart from each other.)

We received an e-mail from her on Dec. 24 that let us know everything was OK: *"The crete is doing fine in the cold. It is drying well inside with woodstoves. It caused condensation on windows and doors etc. I can leave windows open a crack in daytime and helps dry. I didn't put too much on inside or outside cause of the weather turning cold—there is probably 1-2 inches on inside and 2-4 on outside over the polyiso. I will do more next summer. I covered the tops of the domes with heavy black plastic to keep the crete warm and wet off. It helps the snow to slide off."*

Close-up of the pump. The hose at the bottom connects to the tow mixer. The hose at the left hooks up to a diesel-powered air compressor (which cost $100 a day to rent). The hose at the top connects to the spray nozzle shown in the previous photo.

Bette Heeftle can be contacted at 719-256-4075: <bettehef@bwn.net>.

Dylan Roberts sprays papercrete onto the inside of the dome. This is a noisy, dirty job. He is wearing coveralls, goggles, and a dust mask to protect from airborne papercrete particles (the dome was filled with a papercrete fog), and ear protectors to protect against the high-pitched hiss of the spray nozzle.

The last fall we visited Abi David in Crestone, CO and toured her papercrete construction project. This photo of her house was shot from the same angle as the one printed in EQ #4, page 19 (papercrete book, page 63).

143

That's All She Wrote! (For Now)

I am retiring from the publishing business for awhile, so that I can finally get caught up with numerous homestead projects, and so that Laura won't have to think about papercrete while working on her M.S. Therefore, this is the last issue of *Papercrete News*. Each subscriber will receive a refund for the balance of their subscription. Some people might believe I'm doing this because of lack of support, but actually, with 300 subscribers, PCN is wildly successful for a newsletter, and we are refunding several thousand dollars in subscription money.

I'm getting out of the papercrete "biz" because I never intended to play a one-note symphony, which is what papercrete is for me. Papercrete is great stuff with lots of potential, but I became involved with it mainly in an attempt to promote the much more ambitious goal of sustainability through our magazine, **Earth Quarterly**. I never intended to make a career as a "papercrete expert."

In a year or two, after I get caught up with my other projects, I plan to start up *Dry Country News* once again, which is good news for DCN fans. To my surprise, I discovered that it's easier to promote a regional publication than a national one, even though the potential audience for a national publication is 20 times larger. The new DCN will be a 16-page newsletter, and will come out once a year for starters. It will be our usual eclectic blend of interesting, high-quality info— desert living with a sustainability flavor. In time, it's possible that DCN will gather enough support so that I'll be able to put out more pages more frequently... particularly if our era of crazy prosperity ever gives way to something more sane. Like most people living in the Southwest, I love this part of the world, and look forward to putting out a multi-faceted publication about our marvelous bioregion once again.

If you want to subscribe to DCN now, and are willing to wait awhile for your first issue, you can return your refund check, and, if you want, write another check to bring your subscription up to the number of issues you want to receive ($5 per issue).

As for papercrete and fidobe, long may they wave. They have enormous potential, and the curve for them can only be upward. My favorite true story concerns a Doña Ana County, N.M. building inspector who has decided to build his house out of papercrete. With acceptance like that, you just know that papercrete and fidobe are going to catch on big time.

We plan to keep the papercrete website going, with the following URL: <www.zianet.com/papercrete>.

On page 7 of this issue, we tell how to join the papercrete e-group (listserv), how to access the e-group archives, and how to access a list of papercrete builders.

I have written one final papercrete article, which will appear in *BackHome* magazine at the end of the year.

For updates on DCN and EQ (hey, don't count EQ out as long as I'm still breathing!), check our websites:

<www.zianet.com/drynews>
and
<www.zianet.com/earth>.

In conclusion, putting out **Earth Quarterly** and *Papercrete News* has been quite an adventure. Nothing is ever really over, it just morphs into something that appears different to our 3-D eyes, and I'm already looking forward to my next publishing project. Thanks for your support, and may your slurry always come out nice and creamy, and may your stucco never crack.

—Gordon Solberg, Editor

Goodbye to the Papercrete Express!

Well, it's been an interesting ride, The Papercrete Express. When Gordon and I signed up for the Earth Quarterly tour, we didn't realize that we were signing on for the full papercrete immersion. It just seemed to happen around us.

What we really started out to do was meet Earth-friendly type folks doing homestead-like activities, and write good articles about them. We hoped to hook up with our "community," our compadres in aware (or even semi-aware) consumerism. We have few regrets about what we have done; we really did meet loads of very cool, creative and worthy people. That has been delightful.

We are ready to pass the papercrete baton on. We certainly wish all slurry folks the very best. We most wholeheartedly say thanks to all our friends, fans and supporters. Best of luck in all your future adventures.

SLURRY RULES!!!

—Laura Solberg, Publisher

Letters

I subscribe to a number of periodicals, but EQ is perhaps the most provocative and cutting edge. Papercrete is great stuff, and I've been proselytizing it for over a year now; but I'm concerned about two things: its use of cement, and (more importantly) its problems with combustibility.

I'm convinced that you are correct, Gordon, when you say that the future probably belongs to fidobe. I've been experimenting with the stuff and I'd like to share some of my findings with other readers.

I ground up a fair amount of pulped paper with a garbage disposal (it hardens and looks and feels a lot like papercrete), and began mixing it with some local dirt which is about ¾ clay (too high for adobe or cob). The mixture was about ¾ paper by volume, but was probably at least ¾ dirt, by weight.

It works wonderfully. The high clay content binds very well to the pulped paper and is tougher than any adobe or rammed earth I've encountered. It weighs 2/3 oz. per cubic inch, which is about 2/3 the weight of adobe, and has some insulation value (in addition to the great thermal mass). It also looks good, like rich, dark adobe. The real revelation was when I was mixing it. It feels like cottage cheese, very thick and creamy. When a handful is pulled out and balled up, it acts like dough, becoming very easy to form.

When I had added just enough clay-slip to the mixture to coat all the paper fully, I removed a test ball and set it out to dry. This sample ended up being altogether different from anything else I've encountered, so I might as well call it "Light-Clay Fidobe" (conceptually it bears some resemblance to "Leichtlehm," or light-clay straw used as in-fill or insulation). It was probably about 1/6 clay-dirt, just enough to coat the paper fibers, but not enough to pack it down tight, as happens with regular fidobe.

Light-Clay Fidobe is very light, very hard, and it insulates extremely well. After it had fully cured I decided to give it a flame test, since it has such a high paper content. I set it over a candle, just touching the flame, for about half an hour. It insulates marvelously—two inches away from the flame it was barely warm. Later, after it was cold to the touch, I scraped the blackened part off to see if it showed any signs of the papercrete "slow burn." It did not! It had charred about ¼ inch deep, but the char was almost as hard as the uncharred material, and did not remove easily (a far cry from the handful of ashes papercrete becomes...).

Light-Clay Fidobe appears to be an attractive alternative to, or a complement to, papercrete. Light-Clay and regular fidobe promise to revolutionize cob,

ROOF DESIGN *(continued from p. 132)*

A week or so later, we covered the roof with papercrete panels. These were papercrete blocks made specifically for this purpose—they contained only paper and Portland cement, but no sand, to keep the weight down. Each panel was 1 foot wide, 4 feet long, and 4" thick, and contained two pieces of cane serving as "organic rebar" for extra strength. In this photo, Neil Solberg and Justin Jay are carrying a roof block over to Greg Jay, who has laid down a 2" layer of wet slurry, into which the block will be snugged into place.

The roof is nearly covered with the papercrete blocks.

(Continued on p. 150)

wattle and daub, adobe and rammed earth construction—and maybe challenge straw bale. (It will need a good foundation and a break from any wicking action. But then, what doesn't?)

Light-Clay Fidobe is basically non-flammable, it probably insulates as well as papercrete, is substantially harder and tougher than papercrete, requires no cement (no expense!) and is much prettier. It can be trowelled when still wet to a smooth texture with a rich color that may require no interior finish coat, except to seal. Exterior, I see no reason why it can't also be merely sealer and left to gleam in the sun, though that will require more experimentation.

My theory is that clay could be shoveled into a drag mixer instead of Portland cement and sand, and all Mike McCain's forms and methods could be used in the same manner as before (especially the continuous form, "coil pot" method). It's cheaper, less flammable, and better looking (though much slower setting up...).

Jim Burke
P.O. Box 1804
Bisbee, AZ 85603

It sounds like you have some wonderful dirt to work with! Fidobe is definitely the way to go in the Southwest. But I need to emphasize that papercrete will not burn if the mix contains a high enough percentage of nonflammable ingredients—cement and sand.

I have just finished reading the article on papercrete construction in issue No. 179 of *Mother Earth News* and I'm very excited. Papercrete fits closely with construction concepts I've worked with over the past few years which I believe would be cost effective and ecologically sound in a number of ways. For example:

1. Would the addition of horticultural grade perlite or vermiculite increase the R-value while reducing weight of the material without sacrificing strength?

2. Recycled waste, such as shredded plastic, could be added as "fiber" to increase the PSI of the mix.

3. Substituting fly ash could reduce the weight over that of sand.

I've been working on a design for a dome home which uses the principle idea of being able to apply the "stucco" to a wire and rebar frame. This could be done either by hand or as one would apply "shotcrete" or gunnite in swimming pool construction. I'd love to exchange some ideas with PCN readers on this.

Prior to my arrest, my former spouse worked in a recycling plant and I became aware of a number of recycled products which I believe would make a great aggregate for concrete or stucco mixes. Some preliminary tests I did proved promising. Working in the building trades familiarized me with the possibilities of various rebar and wire or mesh reinforcement ideas.

Having once owned my own masonry construction company, I knew what I could build for as low as $1.25 a square foot, labor included!

I'd very much like to discuss some of my ideas further. Ideally I could connect with someone willing to conduct testing for strength, shrinkage, weight, etc.

David Van Orden
ADC# 33321 B 1B9
Cook Unit
Arizona State Prison Complex Eyman
P.O. Box 3200
Florence, AZ 85232

How about a permanent form which would add structural strength, and reduce the volume of papercrete needed? When I hung drywall using steel studs, I was effectively building a series of big, flat boxes. Why not build a 4'x8'x4" steel box, leave out the 12" or 16" on-center studs, and fill the empty box with papercrete? To hold the mud in until the mud sets up, screw a 4'x8'x½" sheet of OSB inside and out and use temporary center braces until dry. By my calculations (which may be wrong—I'm bad at math) it will take 1.7 cu. yds. of papercrete per 4'x8'x4"section.

My personal feeling is that the extra strength and the ease of construction would offset any extra cost, and I'm not sure the steel might be cheaper than wood in the long run. Depending on details such as windows, rebar, etc., 2 people should be able to "frame" or form a 16'x32' small home (like Andy Hopkins') in a day or two. Since the steel all remains in place, stripping the forms is simply removing the braces and 2 sheets of OSB.

Another advantage would be that you could do all plumbing and electrical prior to pouring papercrete. In a fairly simple, small home, this whole process should fly right away.

If I knew some material costs, like steel studs, ½" rebar, etc. I could work out estimates for building the exterior shells for some basic designs. I've been putting my small (500-1200 sq. ft.) homes on paper for about 4 years now. If anyone wants to discuss or share ideas, please feel free to contact me. Living in an 8'x12' box has taught me a lot about utilizing space. This experience should be good for something.

David Van Orden
same address as previous letter

I hope my return address doesn't upset you, yes I am a prisoner in "Old Folsom." I am also a carpenter with over 20 years experience, much of which was in pouring concrete and working with masonry, including cinder "speed blocks." Do they use speed blocks in N.M.? If not, here is a description and 3 view sketch. The design could easily be adapted to papercrete blocks

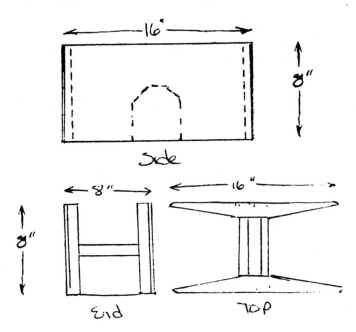

side

End   Top

Cornville Update

In March we visited the house Tim Pye is building in Cornville, AZ (as described in our last issue). Designed by Cathryn Swann and built by Tim Pye, this 3000-square-foot house with 12-inch-thick walls is probably the most massive papercrete structure yet built. Their e-mail address is <wizardmoon@sedona.net>; phone 520-634-1696.

Tim Pye with his newspaper stash, obtained for free from the local newspaper publisher. The house is in the background. The left side shows post-and-beam design; middle shows forms in place to hold papercrete slurry; right side shows poured wall after forms have been removed.

and then just fill the cells with more papercrete! They would also be easier to reinforce than solid blocks.

Speed block description: An 8" high, 8" wide, 16" long cinder block with open ends and a half-height center wall for bond beam. The ends taper on the inside from the center wall to the ends of each block, obviating the need for vertical mortar joints. Size could easily be adapted to 12"x12"x24" for papercrete. In conventional speed blocks you only "butter" the horizontal joint with mortar (papercrete?).

The edge bevel simulates a "v" striker joint on the wall at the ends of each block—not necessary, of course, with papercrete blocks. Even if you left the ends square but open for papercrete blocks you would still gain the primary benefit of speed blocks—a larger unbroken cell for a stronger wall with a cleaner finished appearance than slip forming, and ease of reinforcing the wall with either steel rebar or pre-stressed poly-rope. With square ends you would need to butter the vertical joints.

Also, I would suggest in the sealing of exterior wall surfaces, the use of elastomeric and not a silicone-based compound, as silicone tends to mold (even though you yourselves are in a fairly dry climate) and elastomeric (such as snow roof) cannot mold, but <u>can</u> be painted over, or a tinting agent added before application to the walls. Hope that helps you in some small way.

Robin Sharp H58096
FSP-II Box 715071, B1-A4-22
Represa, CA 95671-5071

Forms this high need to be securely braced.

Papercrete Formulas

There is no "one right" formula. Experiment and see what works best for you.

Regular Papercrete (200 gallon mixer)

160 gallons water
60 lb. paper
94 lb. Portland cement (1 bag)
4 lb. lime (optional)—2 shovels. Lime makes the mix set up faster, and makes a stickier stucco that adheres better.
66 lb. sand—15 shovels

Roof Panel Mix

Same as above, but leave out the sand. Sand (1) adds thermal mass, (2) makes the slurry pack down better for a denser block, and (3) helps prevent stucco from cracking, which are all desirable for blocks or stucco. For roofing, we want light weight and maximum insulation, so we leave out the sand.

Paper Adobe (Fidobe)

160 gallons water
60 lb. paper
240 lb. dirt

The proportion of dirt to paper depends on how heavy a block you want. The less dirt, the lighter the block and the higher the R value. The clay content of the dirt can be anywhere from 30% to 100%. With regular adobe, too high a clay content causes cracking. This is not a problem with paper adobe—the paper fibers prevent cracking. It is good to have at least 30% clay, since clay is the "glue" that helps bond the block together.

Papercrete Formula for Small Mixer (100 gallons)

69 gallons water
25 lb. paper
40 lb. cement
2 lb. lime (optional)
26 lb. sand

Earth Quarterly Papercrete Workshop -- May 14-17, 1999

Afterword

In the three years since I published the first edition of this book, our environmental and political situation has become immeasurably worse. Not only is our environment continuing to degrade at an appalling rate, but our country is under the control of the most anti-environmental regime in history. It's a hell of a predicament, and I'm too much a realist to hold out false hope. The American electorate is thoroughly manipulated, distracted, and entertained, and is complacent to the point of sleepwalking. Corporations rule, and it's a pity. The only antidote I can suggest is the example of Mother Theresa, who, even though she lacked the power to change the overall situation, did the right thing anyway. As long as we can maintain our sense of compassion and good humor, there is hopefully still hope.

About papercrete, I still think it's got lots of potential. Fidobe in particular holds great promise as a building material—it's strong, insulating, Earth-friendly, and virtually free. Of course, we can hardly expect the corporate culture to be very interested in such a material, and I fear that by the time the dominant socio/economic system finally collapses, the Earth will be terminally degraded. Hopefully, sustainability—both as a concept and a superior way of life—will catch on before it's too late. At any rate it will be up to future generations to cope with the mess we have left them.

On a more personal note, my papercrete office is now complete, and I like it. People sometimes ask me if I would do it differently if I had it to do over and I say yes, I would go post-and-beam. I would put in corner posts and have my window frames come all the way down to the ground. I would screw my forms onto the corner posts and window/door frames so that the walls would be straight and plumb. Rather than trying to build a heroically sustainable roof, I would just put up a standard roof. Part of my office roof is papercrete on top, covered with two coats of Homestar silicone sealer, two coats of eslastomeric sealer, and two coats of latex paint. It will be interesting to see how this stands up to the first heavy hail storm. The other part of my roof was built with welded rebar trusses which proved inadequate to hold up the weight of the papercrete blocks I laid over them, so I just built a conventional roof over my failed experiment. It would have been cheaper to have just built a conventional roof in the first place, but experimentation always carries with it the risk of failure, which helps keep things interesting.

Overall, I am pleased with my papercrete office. It's a snug little structure that serves my purposes well. I am glad to see that many other people are picking up the papercrete ball and running with it. I hope that this book has proved informative and inspirational to people who would like to give papercrete a try.

Since I am now totally involved in other things, I am no longer available for papercrete consultations. If you need to have any questions answered, try the "FAQ" section of my papercrete website, or try the other websites listed in the "Resources" section of this book. You can also try the papercrete egroup listed on the "Resources" page.

—March 1, 2002

Then the roof blocks were covered with a final coat of slurry. It is best to double the cement content of this slurry (to 2 bags per 200-gallon batch), to make it as hard as possible. Also, it is best to trowel the slurry as smooth as possible, to save on all the expensive roof coating which will be painted onto the papercrete after it has dried.

Here's a view of the finished roof. The left side of the roof is a conventional design, using 2x6 rafters. The papercrete portion of the roof was painted with two coats of Homestar sealer, followed by two coats of elastomeric roof coating, followed by two coats of tan latex paint. The reason for the latex paint was to help the roof blend into its surroundings. A brilliant white roof is efficient in terms of reflecting solar radiation, but can be an obnoxious eyesore in the landscape.

AN EXPERIMENT NOT TO BE RECOMMENDED

In August 1999 my papercrete office was completed except for the finish work. I had just installed the conventional part of the roof—2x6" rafters covered with 1/2" plywood and metal roofing. I have no estimate of the weight of the roof, but I know it is considerable. There is a lot of weight bearing down on the wall.

Then we had by far the worst flood we have ever had in the 29 years I have lived here. Not only did the Rio Grande top its banks, but it entered my yard and lapped the base of my papercrete office. Since papercrete absorbs moisture, the water wicked up into the wall about a foot higher than the water level.

This photo shows the floodwaters submerging the bottom of the wall, and the water wicking up almost halfway to the windowframe.

This could have been a disaster. I could have ended up with a pile of wet rubble with a heavy metal roof lying on top of it. Fortunately, this did not happen. The wall gradually dried out, and within a couple of months it looked almost as good as new.

It did, however, develop a slight lean—not enough to cause immediate problems, but I decided to lay a new footing along the bottom of the wall, and then I built a 2x4 wall covered with hardboard siding. This wall compensates for the lean, and now supports the roof. None of this would have been necessary if we hadn't had the flood.

But this goes to show that even wet papercrete can support more weight than we might think.